Issued under the authority of the H

CU00663700

# Manual of Firemanship

A survey of the science of fire-fighting

# Book 2
# Fire brigade equipment

London
Her Majesty's Stationery Office

FM 2881 WILLIAMS

First published 1974
Third impression 1984

The structure and publishing
history of the Manual is shown
on pages 197-200

ISBN 0 11 340582 0

# Preface

In this volume—Book No. 2 in the new format of the *Manuals of Firemanship*—the bread and butter items of fire brigade equipment are described. Part 1 is devoted to hose, which forms the basis of the fireman's weapons against fire. Hose is designed to provide a reliable and efficient service only if it is properly used and given correct care and maintenance; improper use may lead to premature failure which can result in greater damage to goods and property than that caused by the fire itself. The fittings which are necessary to enable branches, standpipes, breechings and the various other pieces of equipment to be attached to hose are dealt with in Part 2. Here again proper treatment of hose fittings such as nozzles is stressed if good striking jets are to reach the heart of the fire as even a small deformity or indentation in a nozzle will cause a jet to break up and fail to strike the target.

Part 3 contains a description of ropes and lines as used in the fire service, followed by examples of the various knots and hitches which must be mastered by all firemen, both for hauling and securing lines and equipment, and for personal safety. Finally, in this section the usage of lines and the various methods of stowing and carrying them are described.

The last section, Part 4, is devoted to the miscellaneous items of firemen's equipment which are normally categorised under the generic title of 'small gear'. Here will be found many special tools which have been specifically designed for fire brigade use and which in the past were given some rather odd names such as the 'preventer'—which has now been changed to 'ceiling hook'—and the 'persuader'.

The Home Office is again indebted to all those people who have assisted in the revision of this volume and have helped to ensure that the contents are as up-to-date as possible.

Home Office
September 1973.

# Metrication

List of SI units for use in the fire service.

| Quantity and basic or derived SI unit and symbol | Approved unit of measurement | Conversion factor |
| --- | --- | --- |
| **Length**<br>metre (m) | kilometre (km)<br>metre (m)<br>millimetre (mm) | 1 mile = 1·609 km<br>1 yard = 0·914 m<br>1 foot = 0·305 m<br>1 inch = 25·4 m |
| **Area**<br>Square metre (m$^2$) | square kilometre (km$^2$)<br>square metre (m$^2$)<br>square millimetre (mm$^2$) | 1 mile$^2$ = 2·590 km$^2$<br>1 yard$^2$ = 0·836 m$^2$<br>1 foot$^2$ = 0·093 m$^2$<br>1 inch$^2$ = 645·2 mm$^2$ |
| **Volume**<br>cubic metre (m$^3$) | cubic metre (m$^3$)<br>litre (l) ($10^{-3}$m$^3$) | 1 cubic foot = 0·028 m$^3$<br>1 gallon = 4·546 litres |
| **Volume, flow**<br>cubic metre per second (m$^3$/s) | cubic metre per second (m$^3$/s)<br>litres per minute (1/min = $10^{-3}$m$^3$/min) | 1 foot$^3$/s = 0·028 m$^3$/s<br>1 gall/min = 4·546 1/min |
| **Mass**<br>kilogram (kg) | kilogram (kg)<br>tonne (t)<br>= ($10^3$ kg) | 1 lb = 0·454 kg<br>1 ton = 1·016 t |
| **Velocity**<br>metre per second (m/s) | metre/second (m/s)<br>International knot (kn)<br>kilometre/hour (km/h) | 1 foot/second = 0·305 m/s<br>1 UK knot = 1·853 km/h<br>1 Int. knot = 1·852 km/h<br>1 mile/hour = 1·61 km/h |
| **Acceleration**<br>metre per second$^2$ (m/s$^2$) | metre/second$^2$ (m/s$^2$) | 1 foot/second$^2$ = 0·305 m/s$^2$<br>'g' = 9·81 m/s$^2$ |

| Quantity and basic or derived SI unit and symbol | Approved unit of measurement | Conversion factor |
|---|---|---|
| **Force**<br>newton (N) | kilonewton (kN)<br>newton (N) | 1 ton force $= 9 \cdot 964$ kN<br>1 lb force $= 4 \cdot 448$ N |
| **Energy, work**<br>joule (J)<br>$( = 1$ Nm$)$ | joule (J)<br>kilojoule (kJ)<br>kilowatt-hours (kWh) | 1 British thermal unit<br>$= 1 \cdot 055$ kJ<br>1 foot lb force $= 1 \cdot 356$ J |
| **Power**<br>watt (W)<br>$( = 1$ J/s $= 1$ Nm/s$)$ | kilowatt (kW)<br>watt (W) | 1 horsepower $= 0 \cdot 746$ kW<br>1 foot lb force/second $=$<br>$1 \cdot 356$ W |
| **Pressure**<br>newton/metre$^2$ (N/m$^2$)<br><br>$= 1$ pascal (Pa) | bar $= 10^5$ N/m$^2$<br>millibar (mbar)<br>$( = 10^2$ N/m$^2)$<br>metrehead | 1 atmosphere $=$<br>$101 \cdot 325$ kN/m$^2 =$<br>$1 \cdot 013$ bar<br>1 lb force/in$^2 =$<br>$6894 \cdot 76$ N/m$^2 = 0 \cdot 069$<br>bar<br>1 inch Hg $= 33 \cdot 86$ mbar<br>1 metrehead $= 0 \cdot 0981$ bar<br>1 foot head $= 0 \cdot 305$<br>metrehead |
| **Head, quantity of heat**<br>joule (J) | joule (J)<br>kilojoule (kJ) | 1 British thermal unit<br>$= 1 \cdot 055$ kJ |
| **Heat flow rate**<br>watt (W) | watt (W)<br>kilowatt (kW) | 1 British thermal unit/<br>hour $= 0 \cdot 293$ W<br>1 British thermal unit/<br>second $= 1 \cdot 055$ kW |
| **Specific energy, calorific value specific latent heat**<br>joule/kilogram<br>(J/kg)<br>joule/m$^3$ (J/m$^3$) | kilojoule/kilogram<br>(kJ/kg)<br>kilojoule/m$^3$ (kJ/m$^3$)<br>megajoule/m$^3$ (MJ/m$^3$) | 1 British thermal unit/<br>lb $= 2 \cdot 326$ kJ/kg<br>1 British thermal<br>unit/ft$^3 = 37 \cdot 26$ kJ/m$^3$ |
| **Temperature**<br>degree Celsius (°C) | degree Celsius (°C) | 1 degree centigrade $=$<br>1 degree Celsius |

# Contents

# Part 1
# Hose

# Part 2
# Hose fittings

## Chapter 8 Breechings, adaptors, miscellaneous hose fittings and ramps

# Part 3
# Ropes and lines

## Chapter 9 Construction of rope

## Chapter 10 Deterioration of rope

## Chapter 11 Lines used in the fire service

# Part 4

# Small gear and miscellaneous equipment

# List of plates

# Part 1
# Hose

Fire hose has been used for hundred of years for the extinguishment of fire and is one of the basic elements of the fireman's stock-in-trade. It is necessarily for the conveyance of water from static supply sources or from mains hydrants on to the fire. In areas where water may be in short supply, hose may be necessary to relay water considerable distances, and special large diameter hose has been designed for this purpose.

In this Part, the various types of hose in general use by fire brigades are described. Broadly, hose may be divided into two categories according to its main use: 'delivery' hose is laid on the delivery side of the pump where the water passing through it is at a pressure greater than that of the atmosphere, and 'suction' hose, which is employed on the suction side of the pump where the water passing through it may be at a pressure either below or above that of the atmosphere.

Delivery hose may be further divided into: unlined hose, woven from vegetable fibres; non-percolating hose, consisting of a jacket woven from vegetable fibres and having a rubber or plastics lining, a synthetic fibre jacket and lining, or a combination of both natural and synethic fibres, and lining; or hose for hose reels, normally of rubber with fabric reinforcement.

Suction hose includes various types of armoured hose which are constructed to withstand external atmospheric pressure.

# Chapter 1
# General characteristics and specifications

## 1 JCDD Specifications

The following specifications for hose for fire brigade use, prepared for the Central Fire Brigades Advisory Council by the Joint Committee on Design and Development of Appliances and Equipment, are issued by the Home Office and the Scottish Home and Health Department:

JCDD/1/1    Delivery hose, non-percolating.
JCDD/1/2    Delivery hose, unlined.
JCDD/2      Suction hose.
JCDD/7      Hose-reel hose.

The sizes of hose covered by the specifications are those in general use by fire brigades, and for delivery hose are 45, 70 and 90 mm internal diameter; for suction hose 76, 102 and 140 mm internal diameter; and for hose-reel hose 19 mm internal diameter.

## 2 Characteristics of hose

The main characteristics essential for a good fire-fighting hose are:

### a. Flexibility

Hose must be sufficiently flexible to enable it to be handled easily and without kinking when in use, and for it to be made up into a smooth roll whether wet or dry. As regards unlined hose, the canvas has also to be woven tightly enough to ensure that the leakage is small when under pressure. It is possible for manufacturers to produce a hose that is practically watertight, but this has the disadvantage that it is then almost inflexible, and is easily damaged by chafing.

### b. Durability

The durability and wearing qualities must be as high as possible, and the materials used, particularly in the warp, must have high resistance to abrasion and be able to withstand the rough usage which hose inevitably receives in service. Some manufacturers have introduced a tough plastics outer cover to give additional protection to the jacket, and to prolong the life of the hose.

It is also essential that hose is easily repairable by simple means, as, however good a hose may be initially, bursts will occur through damage or other reasons during use.

## c. Resistance to rot

Natural fibres such as flax and cotton are liable to be affected by mildew or rot, and it is important that these materials, when used in the construction of hose, are given rot-proofing treatment. The JCDD specifications require that the materials from which hose is made should be as resistant to mildew as possible.

## d. Change in length and diameter

Any increase in the length or diameter of hose when under pressure indicates that the materials are stretching. Unlimited stretch would tend to weaken the hose, and bursts, particularly of the weft, would occur: moreover, lengthwise stretch or extension causes hose to snake when under pressure.

The JCDD specifications require the construction of hose to be such that the length and diameter are not unduly affected when under pressure, and maximum limits are laid down. The limit of extension of unlined hose at a pressure of 12 bar is 6 per cent of the length when dry, and the increase in diameter of the 70 mm size hose is limited to 2·4 mm.

As nylon and terylene are used extensively in jackets on non-percolating hose, a larger increase in diameter (6 mm for 70 mm hose) is permitted to allow for the greater stretch properties of these materials.

Even with these limits it will be seen that the extension in 30·5 m of hose may be as much as 1·8 m. This increase in length emphasises the inadvisability of straightening out charged hose. Should a length burst and require to be changed the contraction of the line on release of tension resulting from the loss of pressure would pull the couplings of the lengths at either end so far apart that a new length could not be connected up.

## e. Frictional loss

A rough internal surface increases the resistance to the flow of water through hose; the surface should therefore be as smooth as possible in order to reduce to a minimum loss of pressure through friction. The JCDD specifications require the internal surface of all hose to be as smooth as possible.

## f. Weight

The weight of hose is important, not only from the point of view of handling at fires and drills, but also as regards stowage on appliances. Heavy hose is usually bulky, and such a combination may present problems insofar as the load-carrying capacity of an appliance is concerned, and as regards the locker space available. The JCDD specifications require hose to be as light as possible without sacrificing durability. The maximum weight limit laid down for 70 mm non-percolating hose is 624 g per metre.

Manufacturers are able to produce good quality hose within the limits of the JCDD specifications, and the use of synthetic materials and lightweight linings has enabled manufacturers to produce a good non-percolating hose having a weight of about 510 g per metre.

## g. Hose pressures and acceptance tests

Hose has to withstand high internal pressures. During fire fighting these pressures may be as high as 10·5 bar and shock pressures may be even higher. Hose must be designed to give an adequate margin over pressure likely to be encountered, and it is usually constructed to withstand at least twice the pressure to which it is likely to be subjected in service. Manufacturers sometimes indicate the average burst pressure of their various hoses. This is referred to as the 'short length burst pressure' and may be as high as 41 bar depending on the type and quality of the hose.

Formerly the JCDD specifications required a sample, cut from any length of hose selected at random, to withstand a pressure of 34·5 bar for non-percolating hose. This has been changed and the requirement is now that each actual length of hose be tested to a pressure of 20·7 bar. The testing of every length to a pressure about double the maximum likely to be met with in use is regarded as a better test of quality than merely selecting short lengths at random and subjecting them to pressures three or four times greater than the hose is likely to incur in service.

Acceptance tests are usually carried out at the manufacturers' works.

# Chapter 2
# Delivery hose

The first hose used was made of leather. It was made only in short lengths owing to its great weight, and this, added to the fact that it had to be periodically greased to keep it pliable, made it very difficult to handle. The hose was riveted throughout its length (Fig. 2.1) and replacing a rivet in the centre of a length was a major operation. The rivet was first inserted, then a mandrel

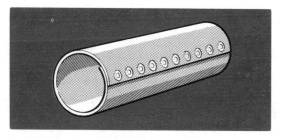

Fig. 2.1 Sketch showing a piece of old leather hose.

was passed into the hose to act as a seating for the rivet while the washer was put on and clinched.

Leather hose was followed by hose constructed of natural fibres. This was known as canvas hose and was first manufactured in Scotland about 1850. The fibres used were flax, and the hose was woven entirely by hand. It was, of course, unlined and relied on the swelling of the fibres when wet to effect a measure of water tightness.

The disadvantage of water seepage from canvas hose was later overcome by inserting a waterproof lining after the hose was woven. This hose was known as 'rubber-lined hose', but following the use of synthetic materials for hose construction the term *non-percolating* is now used in the fire service to describe all types of lined hose irrespective of the materials used. Hand weaving for fire hose has now been superseded by machine weaving.

## 1 Unlined hose

Unlined hose is made chiefly from flax, although hemp, cotton, ramie and some other less known vegetable fibres have also been used to a limited extent. Flax is probably the world's oldest vegetable fibre, and because of its strength, durability and absorbent qualities, it has been used for fire brigade hose for many years. Nowadays, however, almost all fire brigades in the United Kingdom have ceased to use unlined hose, especially as the high price of flax has now made top quality unlined hose considerably more expensive than a good quality non-percolating hose. Hemp as usually available makes a very stiff hose and one which is subject to rapid deterioration in use. It has been found that a hemp weft with a flax warp makes a hose of fair quality, but only when soft hemp of the best quality is used; hemp is not therefore used in the manufacture of hose for fire brigade use in the United Kingdom. Cotton has only been used experimentally for unlined hose and the experiments have not been successful. It is, however, used in the manufacture of jackets for non-percolating hose.

Many experiments have been carried out in making unlined hose from synthetic fibres, but mainly because of their lack of absorbency, it is not possible to produce with these materials a watertight hose of sufficient flexibility for fire brigade use. A recent development by one manufacturer makes use of synthetic fibres for other than non-percolating hose. This new type of hose is called *percolised hose*. It has a special type of lining and the jacket is woven from cotton and synthetic fibre yarns. It is manufactured under a patented process by means of which the amount of percolation or seepage through the walls of the hose can be controlled within required limits.

The fabric of canvas hose consists of two sets of yarns running at right angles to each other (Fig. 2.2), those running lengthwise being called the *warp* and those running crosswise, the *weft*.

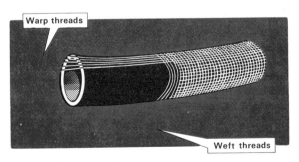

Fig. 2.2 Sketch showing 'warp' and 'weft' threads.

The *weft* generally consists of from ten to twenty-four single strands or plies, twisted together, and the *warp* of from three to nine strands twisted together. The warp threads in hose are those that give it durability to resist wear and tear, while the weft threads resist the tendency of water pressure to burst the hose. For this reason the weaving is so arranged that the warp threads are on the outside and they can be clearly seen when looking at the hose (Fig. 2.3).

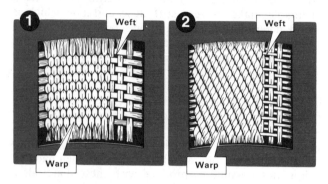

Fig. 2.3 Examples of (1) 'plain' weave and (2) 'twill' weave.

Hose is woven in two ways, *plain* and *twill*. In plain woven hose (Fig. 2.3(1)), the warp threads are woven under one and over one throughout the fabric. This type is normally used for unlined hose. In twill woven hose (Fig. 2.3(2)), the warp threads are woven on the principle of over two and under one; this weave is more pliable, and is usually used for lined hose. It is utilised particularly with heavy rubber linings so as to obtain maximum flexibility. However, due to the introduction of lightweight linings, the need for the flexibility of twill woven hose is less important, and most hose is now plain woven.

Hose is woven on either flat or circular looms. Both types of loom produce a satisfactory hose, but other factors being equal, flat-woven hose is generally weaker at the selvedges or longitudinal creases. The hose produced by circular looms is capable of withstanding greater pressures than hose of equal construction made on flat looms, and circular woven hose (Plate 1) has now entirely superseded flat woven hose for fire brigade use.

It has been the practice for many years to treat hose manufactured from vegetable fibre with a rot-proofing agent. At one time hose was given a zinc chloride treatment, known as *burnettising*, but more effective preservative agents are now available, and burnettising with zinc chloride has been superseded by the use of an agent based on pentachlorophenyl laurate. Hose may be given this rot-proofing treatment during manufacture, or the yarn may be treated before being woven.

# 2 Non-percolating hose

The term *non-percolating* is now used to describe all types of non-porous delivery hose including rubber-lined and the many combinations of hose manufactured from synthetic materials. For many years the main type of non-porous delivery hose in use was rubber lined; this consisted of a normal woven flax hose (known as a 'jacket') into which was inserted a rubber lining. Owing to the limitation in the supply of flax during World War II, cotton-jacketed rubber-lined hose was imported, mainly from the USA, where it was used extensively. The chief disadvantages of cotton-jacketed hose are that it is heavy, it occupies more space than conventional types of hose and has less flexibility (particularly when wet), which makes it difficult to handle. With the increasing use of synethic materials, hose with an all-cotton jacket is now obsolete.

Rubber-lined hose was at one time inclined to be heavy and bulky, but in recent years the weights of lined hoses have been very much reduced by the use of other linings. The increasing availability of synthetic materials such as nylon, terylene and plastics, has also opened up a new field for the manufacture of fire hose. Manufacturers now use rubber and synthetic materials to produce a lightweight rot-resisting non-porous hose, at the same time preserving flexibility and durability. It is of interest to note that the weight of some of these new lightweight hoses is about 510 g per metre as against the 800 to 850 g of the old or conventional rubber-lined hose. The manufacturers claim that the better qualities of lightweight hose will enable it to withstand burst pressures equal to the older type of rubber-lined hose.

## a. Materials used

The materials in general use for the manufacture of non-percolating hose jackets are:

### (1) Flax

Flax has great strength and durability, with high absorbent qualities, but when wet adds greatly to the weight of lined hose. It also needs rot-proofing treatment.

### (2) Cotton

Cotton has strength and high resistance to abrasion, but like flax it also has high absorbent qualities and needs rot-proofing treatment.

### (3) Nylon

Nylon (the registered trade name of polymeric amide plastics) is a synthetic rot-resisting fibre, light in weight and of great strength, with a low degree of absorbency. Nylon stretches considerably under pressure, and its use for fire hose is normally confined to the weft. If it were used in the warp, the stretch might result in undue 'snaking' of the hose.

(4) Terylene

Terylene (the registered trade name of polyester plastics) is a synthetic rot-resisting fibre of light weight and great strength with low absorbent qualities. It resists stretching to a greater extent than other synthetic fibres and may be used for both warp and weft. When it is used in the warp, 'snaking' of the hose under pressure is greatly reduced.

Hose jackets are made with these materials in various combinations, and the following are some typical examples:

| Weft | Warp |
|------|------|
| Flax | Flax |
| Nylon | Flax |
| Terylene | Flax |
| Nylon | Cotton |
| Terylene | Cotton |
| Terylene | Terylene |

The materials used to make these jackets non-percolating may be either rubber or synthetic. The rubber may be in the form of calendered sheet, extruded tube or latex, and in some cases the latex is reinforced with cotton. Elastomeric material with a low compression set may be used as an internal lining, but generally natural or synthetic rubber is used. Lined hose may have a plastics extruded covering.

## b. Construction

Jackets for non-percolating hose are woven on circular looms and may be either of plain or twill weave; plain weave is, however, more generally used. The type of material used and the method employed for making the jackets non-percolating varies with each manufacturer and rubber or plastics may be used in combination with any of the jackets listed in (a) above. The principal methods of lining and covering are briefly as follows:

(1) Rubber linings

A tube of rubber is extruded to the correct size to fit the hose. The hose jacket is laid out full length on a special bench and is held in position while the lining is drawn into it by means of a line. If the lining is already cured, a liquid adhesive is poured between the lining and the jacket. If the lining is not cured, no adhesive is necessary. One end of the hose is then connected to a steam pipe and the other end is blanked off except for a small drain cock. The hose is then put under steam pressure which causes the lining to become fused to the jacket. The steam pressure used is about 3·5 bar and the pressure is maintained for the time necessary to vulcanise the lining.

## (2) Reinforced latex lining

A cotton fabric is given a number of costs of latex and formed into a tube of suitable size. This is then drawn into, and vulcanised to, the jacket (Plate 2).

## (3) Unreinforced latex lining

Liquid latex is introduced under pressure into the hose in the vertical position. After filling the hose with latex and leaving sufficient time for it to adhere to the jacket, the surplus latex is run out. The process is repeated according to the number of coats required.

## (4) Plastics outer covers

When hose is given a plastics outer cover, it is usually done after the lining has been inserted by pulling the hose and lining into an extruded cover. The whole is bonded together under heat and pressure in one process. Alternatively, the plastics material may be applied in such a way that it penetrates the jacket and forms both a lining and outer cover.

# 3 Hose-reel hose

Hose-reel hose is a non-percolating delivery hose of small internal diameter, normally 19 mm and is used for taking a hose line quickly into buildings using the available water supply on the appliance. It is carried on a drum, and for this reason it has to be flexible, yet it must not flatten unduly when coiled on the drum.

The construction may vary with different types, but generally consists of an inner rubber tube or lining reinforced by wrapping with layers or plies of rubberised woven fabric, applied spirally. An outer cover of abrasion-resistant rubber is then applied and the whole is vulcanised together (Fig. 2.4(1)). Sometimes a braided reinforcement is used (Fig. 2.4(2)). In this case the inner core is passed through a machine which plaits the braided reinforcing layer in position on the tube. This tube is subsequently covered with its outer layer of rubber, and is then vulcanised.

JCDD/7, the requirement specification for hose-reel hose for fire brigade use, has been revised recently to cover types of hose required for use with high pressure hose-reel pumps, such as the Godiva UMP (see the *Manual, Part 2: Chapter 1, 'Pumps, primers and pumping appliances'*. Although rubber hose-reel hose is the only type used in this country at the present time, the specification does not rule out the possible use of alternative materials, such as plastics.

Another specification which, however, relates only to rubber hose-reel hose, is British Standard 3169. This covers four grades of hose, three of which are suitable for use on fire brigade appliances and have a range of working pressures up to 40 bar. BS 3169 may therefore be used as an alternative specification to JCDD/7, provided that the appropriate grade of hose within that standard is specified.

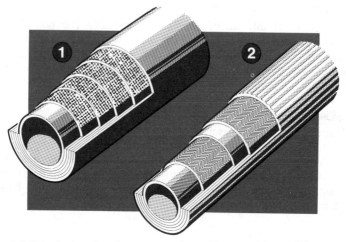

Fig. 2.4 Sketch showing the construction of hose-reel hose: (1) wrapped type; (2) braided type.

## 4 Damage to hose

Emphasis has been laid on the method of fabrication of hose in order that its liability to damage can be fully appreciated. It is important that every fireman should know how to look after the hose in his care and how to keep it in first-class condition, ready for any calls which may be made upon it. Much of the damage caused too hose is avoidable by the strict carrying out of hose drill instructions, and every opportunity should be taken to impress on personnel the necessity for care in the use of hose. It should be emphasised that a high degree of skill and wide experience are needed for the manufacture, testing and maintenance of hose. This should prove an added incentive to the careful and intelligent use of hose.

The causes of decay in hose are:

    (a) abrasion;
    (b) mildew;
    (c) shock;
    (d) acids, oils, grease and petrol.

## a. Abrasion

Men should always be taught to lay out hose without dragging it. The question of abrasion is intimately connected with the methods of making-up hose, and these are dealt with below. Numerous different methods have been developed for storing hose, and these may be listed as:

(1) the roll (or coil);
(2) Dutch roll (or roll on the bight);
(3) flaking;
(4) figure of eight.

### (1) The roll or coil

In this method the hose is laid out flat on the ground and a start is made at the female coupling end (Fig. 2.5, *left*). The coupling

Fig. 2.5 Left: The method of starting to roll a length of hose with instantaneous couplings. Right: the roll of hose completed and secured with a hose strap.

is doubled down on the hose which is then rolled up until the farther end is reached. The hose strap is finally passed through the centre of the hose and secured about 150 mm behind the outer coupling (Fig. 2.5, *right*). Rolled hose is normally to be preferred, since with instanteous couplings, the female couping may be held with both hands and the hose then rotates as it is run out. The correct position in which to hold a roll of hose is shown in Fig. 2.6. Rolled hose should always be stowed on edge, as shown on the right in Fig. 2.5, and never flat. If it is placed flat, the edges are subjected to more than their fair share of wear and tear. A roll of hose, either wet or dry, should never be dragged along the

Fig. 2.6 Correct method of holding a roll of hose with instantaneous couplings for running out.

ground. It may be the easy way, but it is the wrong way. Rolled hose should always be carried.

(2) Dutch roll, or roll on the bight

The hose should be laid out flat on the ground and the female coupling should be drawn back along the hose towards the other end, so that the female coupling lies on top of the hose and about 1m short of the male coupling (Fig. 2.7). After the upper layer

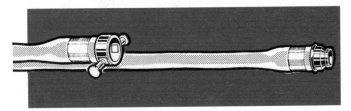

Fig. 2.7 Correct layout of couplings for making a Dutch roll.

has been arranged exactly over the lower layer, the hose is rolled up from the bight so that the couplings come together on the outside of the roll.

To run out hose made up in this manner, both couplings are held and the roll is given a push, when it will roll out and uncoil itself, leaving a long loop of hose. The male coupling is then attached to the pump or standpipe outlet and the female coupling is taken towards the fire. Hose should never be made up in a Dutch roll when it is wet as the tight folds provided by rolling it from the bight are likely to damage the fabric.

### (3) Flaking

In this method the hose is doubled back and forward on itself, and is subsequently secured at the centre of the folds (Fig. 2.8(1)). Its principal advantage is that it permits of running out as fast as

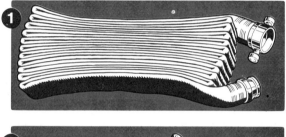

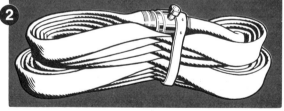

Fig. 2.8 Sketch showing (1) flaked hose, and (2) hose made up as a figure-of-eight.

a man can move, but flaked hose is subject to risk of serious damage due to dragging, particularly over broken glass. This may, to a considerable extent, be obviated by carrying the hose on the shoulder and allowing it to pay out as the man moves away.

The objection to flaking, however, does not apply to hose carried on hose-laying vehicles, as there is little likelihood of dragging when hose is laid from such vehicles. Hose should never be flaked when wet since flaking causes undue strain at the bends.

## (4) Figure-of-eight

This is a variation of flaking, but it avoids the sharp ends. As the name implies, it is wound in a figure-of-eight pattern over two bollards (Fig. 2.8(2)). Its chief advantage is that it avoids the tight bends of flaking and the hose can be run out equally well. On the other hand it takes up considerably more room. This method is undoubltedly the best for storing rubber-lined hose.

## (5) General considerations

Considerable damage is caused by abrasion of hose lengths on rough surfaces, even a concrete yard being rough in this sense, and abrasion is liable to take place more readily and more rapidly when the hose is wet. Places particularly affected are at bends and on the edges of flattened hose. Hose should, therefore, never be dragged along the ground if it can be carried, and it should never be pulled round a corner where it may scrape against a wall. Sufficient slack should be available at the branch so that it may be worked forward without dragging the entire hose line.

The vibration of a pump in continued action may subject the first length of delivery hose to severe chafing at the first point where it touches the ground. A hose bandage, or a short piece of old hose (carried for the purpose), or even sacking, wrapped round at the point of contact, should be fitted to protect the hose from damage. Hose should also be given protection at other points of contact, e.g. copings, sills, etc.

### b. Mildew

Rotting by mildew is a serious cause of deterioration of hose. Its onset is insidious and frequently its presence can only be detected by the most careful and minute examination, although in bad cases it may be recognised by its characteristic 'mouldy' smell. It is not unknown for an apparently sound piece of hose to be so weakened by mildew that it can be pulled apart in the hands.

Mildew is a fungus which, given suitable conditions of moisture and heat, lives and grows in the cellulose of natural fibres such as flax and cotton. Hose insufficiently dried after use or stored in a damp state provides the conditions which promote the growth of mildew, and if the necessary amount of preservative is not present the fabric can be quickly destroyed.

Synthetic materials are not affected by mildew, but the fungus may grow on them if damp and dirt are present. Although mildew has no deleterious effects on synthetic yarn proper, care should be exercised.

Reference has already been made on page 8 to the anti-rot treatment given to natural fibres used in the manufacture of hose.

This rot-proofing treatment gives general protection throughout the life of the hose provided that reasonable care is also taken (see Section 5 below).

In cases where hose has not been subject to rot-proofing treatment, investigation suggests that given the right moisture and temperature together with lack of ventilation, the attack by mildew and subsequent roting of the hose could be very rapid. Complete saturation prevents active infection as readily as complete dryness, and it seems to be established that imperfect drying provides conditions for mildew infection. If suitable drying of fire hose can be guaranteed, there need be no mildew problem.

In 1938–39 the following experiment was carried out:

Of two 1 metre pieces of new 70 mm rubber-lined twill-woven flax hose, one was kept in the relatively dry hose room, the other was hung in the open under head cover for 12 hours for 'conditioning'. The following are the results of destruction tests carried out on a number of the pieces.

|  | *Burst pressure* (*bar*) |
|---|---|
| Hose room pieces | 60 53 62 50 50 55 |
| Conditioned pieces | 65 75 67 70 70 65 |

It seems reasonable to assert that conditioning does increase substantially the pressure resisting and tensile strength of hose. The fundamental necessity is therefore to carry out instructions regarding early cleaning, repairing and reasonably quick drying, preferably in a current of air. When stowing in appliances or storing in hose rooms, adequate ventilation must be ensured by opening the shutter, etc., on hose lorries, lockers and boxes on other appliances and by all methods practicable in hose stores. These precautions should ensure conditioning and prevent mildew.

### c. Shock

It is not generally realised that shock is a frequent cause of hose failure. Hose should invariably be treated with care and rolls of hose should never be thrown roughly to the ground even though they may be dry and in good condition. Shock may, of course, also rise when water is allowed to flow too rapidly into a line of hose which is badly kinked; the sudden straightening out of hose under pressure and the ensuing rush of water which flows only to be checked by the next kink, sets up a series of pressure waves which may easily lead to a burst at a weak point. Similarly a burst may also occur if a hand-controlled branch is shut off suddenly, or when a line is recharged too rapidly after a temporary shut-down.

### d. Acids, oils, grease and petrol

Some types of fire hose are liable to damage by contract with acid, oil, grease, petrol, etc., and hose should be taken when working at oil installations and industrial undertakings to ensure that as far as possible hose has the minimum of contact with oils and the like. Petrol, for example, will cause rubber to separate from the fabric.

### e. Rubber acid

During World War II there were inevitably occasions when rubber-lined hose was stored without being properly drained, and after a time the pockets of water which formed in the hose became acid. This acid was formed by the action of a micro-organism on the sulphur used for vulcanising the ruber, and consisted of dilute sulphuric acid. This was termed *rubber acid*. As the water evaporated through slow drying out, the acid concentration increased and if this acid came into contact with the jacket serious weakening occurred. Hose jackets contaminated by rubber acid may have yellowish or brownish stains.

With the high standard of hose maintenance prevalent in fire brigades today, the formation of rubber acid is unlikely to arise. Some manufacturers recommend that if rubber-lined hose is stored for a long period, particularly in unavoidably hot conditions, water should be passed through it occasionally to keep the lining damp. The amount of water left in the hose after it has been drained is unlikely to be sufficient to permit the formation of any quantity of acid; nevertheless, the possibility of acid forming under these conditions should not be overlooked.

The composition of rubber for lining hoses is chosen nowadays with a view to preventing as far as possible the formation of rubber acid, and this is a requirement of the JCDD specification referred to earlier in this chapter.

## 5 Care of hose

The following are general hints on the care of hose which will assist in prolonging its life:

(i)    New hose should never be allowed to remain in the cases in which it is received, but should be removed and the coils loosened.

(ii)   Hose should be stored in a cool, dry, well-ventilated place.

(iii)  When storing hose, short bends should be avoided as much as possible. If it is necessary to store hose in folds, the bends should be moved now and then to prevent the fabric, and in particular the rubber lining, from taking a permanent set at the bends.

(iv) Hose which is unused for long periods of time should not be allowed to remain on the appliances, but should be removed and placed on racks or towers.

(v) Rubber-lined hose should have water passed through it from time to time to keep the lining in good condition, after which it should be thoroughly drained and dried in towers or by hanging in a warm room.

(v) If hose becomes frozen it should on no account be bent, as it will be liable to crack.

(vii) Rubber deteriorates more rapidly at high temperatures, so rubber-lined hose should not be exposed to hot dry air nor stored in the sun's rays.

(viii) Great care should always be taken of rubber-lined hose, especially when cooling down after large fires, as the hose is often stretched over debris fallen into the building, and as the bricks and stone retain heat for a long time, the outer covering is liable to scorching, so weakening it and shortening the life of the hose.

(ix) Hose should *never* be bent or kept at too acute an angle, especialy under water pressure, since this cause a severe strain on the fibre and is a frequent source of actual breakage, particularly if the edge under strain is rubbed sharply or knocked against a hard surface.

(x) Hose which is laid across roads should always be ramped to prevent damage by passing vehicles. There are several types of ramp and these are described on pages 87 and 92. Every pumping appliance should carry ramps, the number and disposition of which may vary with the accommodation available.

(xi) Hose known to have been contaminated with acids or alkalis should be thoroughly washed immediately with clean water.

(xii) Hose should be drained by under-running. When under-running, it is essential to see that kinks do not form at the bends. These kinks may lead to the formation of pockets of water, or, alternatively, pockets of vacuum, and thus prevent the complete removal of the water. Men must *not* be allowed to walk on hose in order to flatten it out or rid it of water before rolling. This not only drives any flints or grit which may be present right into the fabric, but also imposes a heavy strain on the fibres on either fold which considerably weakens the hose. In practice it is found that bursts almost invariably appear at the two opposite points on the diameter where the hose has been flattened. With lined hose avoidance of such treatment becomes of even greater importance, since its result is that not only are the fibres of the jacket weakened but the lining itself becomes fretted and particles of dirt, etc.

lodge in these frets causing a rapid deterioration of the
rubber. The correct method of clearing water by underrun-
ning is to raise the hose shoulder high (Fig. 2.9) at the
same time avoiding kinks which will trap the water.

Fig. 2.9 Correct method of holding hose to under-run.

(xiii) Rolled or coiled hose is preferable to that made up by
other methods, especially for stowing on appliances, as
the coils are less acute and less liable to damage than, for
example, hose made up on the Dutch roll. In the Dutch
roll, the first few coils from the bight are usually particularly tight and liable to damage the hose if left in this
condition for long periods.

(xiv) When making-up hose on the roll, the female coupling
should not be doubled down on to the hose too tightly,
and the first coil should be somewhat loose. This will
minimise the possibility of the coupling edge cutting into
the hose, and additionally in the case of lined hose, of
the lining becoming separated from the jacket due to
strain. In this connection it is advisable to examine couplings periodically and remove all burrs which might cause
damage.

(xv) Care should be taken when hose is stowed on appliances
to avoid the possibility of the hose chafing against the
locker sides due to vibration.

(xvi) Appliance locker doors should be opened at frequent
intervals to allow air to circulate and condition the hose.

## 6 Cleaning hose

Whenever hose is returned to the station after use it is essential that it should be washed with the greatest care to remove all particles of grit which may have become caught up in the outer fibres. On no account should chemicals of any sort, soap or other material be used in these cleaning operations except as mentioned below. The hose should be laid out straight and flat on a clean surface and clean water applied without force. Careful scrubbing with bristle brooms is generally sufficient to ensure the well-being of canvas and other hose that has no protective outer cover. The brooms used should, as far as possible, have long bristles and not be too stiff, otherwise the grit may be brushed with such force that it cuts the fibres. The motion of the brush should be from side to side and not lengthwise, since, owing to the construction of the hose, the tendency would be for particles to become lodged in the weft. Modern hoses with their various types of plastics outer cover can generally be cleaned by using only running water or even by wiping down with a wet cloth according to circumstances.

Experiments have shown that the fabric of hose which has become begrimed with grease or oil can be cleaned effectively if the hose is scrubbed thoroughly with a solution of soft soap and soda in warm water, and afterwards very thoroughly rinsed in clean cold water. This method may also be used to clean hose that has been in contact with acid. When hose is thickly coated with gummy rubber, grease, etc, fine sawdust can be used to amalgamate with the soiling matter, after which it can be rubbed off without damage to the hose.

When the hose is thoroughly clean, it is best drained by attaching one coupling to a hose whip and running it up the hose tower. Alternatively, lengths of 25 m and upwards should be folded coupling to coupling, the hose whip toggle inserted in the

Toggle

Fig. 2.10 Placing the bight of a length of hose on a hose whip toggle.

bight as shown in Fig. 2.10, and the hose then hung double. When lengths are frequently used, washed and dried, the position of the bight on the toggle should be varied from time to time. The preliminary drying may be effected in the tower and the hose later transfered to the hose drying room. When hose is hung up to drain and dry the couplings should be clear of the ground. In circumstances where couplings are likely to swing, they should be lashed to prevent damage to them and to the hose.

# 7 Drying hose

Hose constructed from natural fibres should be dried until it is soft and pliable. The time required for drying depends on the facilities available and atmospheric drying may take several days, particularly if weather conditions are bad. With the increasing use of synthetic fibres in hose construction, particularly in the weft, the hose drying problem is becoming less difficult. Synthetic fibres absorb little water and the time required to dry the hose is reduced, or in some cases may be dispensed with after the hose has been drained. However, where natural fibre is used in combination with synthetic fibre in the construction of the hose, such hose should always be adequately dried.

There are two methods of drying hose:

- (a) natural;
- (b) mechanical.

## a. Natural drying

The most satisfactory natural method of drying hose is in suitably constructed hose-drying premises which are fully ventilated and yet do not admit rain. Such hose-drying arrangements must depend to a very large extent on local conditions and on local ingenuity. At most stations where fire-fighting equipment is housed, if a hose tower is not available, it is possible to hang the hose from a bracket attached to an outside wall, preferably a wall facing south, subject to the proviso that rubber-lined hose should not be exposed for any considerable length of time to direct sun's rays in hot weather.

The bracket should be fitted with a pulley block. A line (the hose whip) should be rove through the pulley block and one end should terminate with a wooden toggle about 200 mm long. The standing part of the line should be spliced round one end of the toggle. A short length of line having an eye should be spliced into the standing part of the line, thus serving the other end of the wooden toggle over which the hose would be placed prior to hauling aloft. The spare end of the line should be secured close to the toggle, thus making an endless line for ease of working. Hose-drying towers combined with drill towers having one or more sides weatherboarded, have also been in use for some years, and have been found to serve satisfactorily.

Drying sheds might be built on the side of a building with louvre walls, so arranged as to permit of the entry of as much air as possible. Hose might be laid horizontally on racks or hung in folds. If the latter, careful under-running of all hose is essential to remove all the water possible.

Another method of drying hose is to flake it over poles suspended from the roof of a room (e.g. a recreation room or lecture hall) where there is plenty of ventilation and, preferably, some form of heating. When this method is used the hose should be firmly secured to prevent its being damaged by abrasion; the couplings should also be lashed.

## b. Mechanical drying

A number of mechanical hose-drying methods have been developed. The basic principles in every case are the same and consist of the application of warmth and the passage of an adequate current of air to carry away the moisture. The means whereby this is effected vary from what is perhaps the most simple method of heating by radiator in a combined drill and hose-drying tower (see Plates 5 and 6) to an elaborate purpose-built plant which will completely dry saturated unlined hose in a few hours.

### (1) Hose-drying plant

Modern hose-drying plant generally consists of a brick building having a number of drying chambers. The precise number of chambers depends on the maximum quantity of hose likely to be dried at any one time, but each will take up to 20 lengths of hose laid out full length for drying. The hoses are coupled to manifolds through which heated air is blown; in addition heated air is circulated by a fan to assist in drying the outside of the hose. An extraction fan in each chamber maintains a constant circulation of air.

Operating temperatures of the plant as recommended by the manufacturers should be carefully observed and should it be necessary to dry non-percolating hose in the plant, it is advisable that the hose manufacturers be consulted as to the maximum drying temperature to which their hose should be subjected. Too high a temperature may damage the lining and perhaps affect its adhesion to the outer cover. Overheading of unlined hose tends to make the fibres brittle and weaken them.

### (2) Hose-drying cabinets

Other hose-drying machines work on the principle of a cabinet in which the hose is contained in long bights (Plate 3). The interior of the cabinet is warmed and ventilated by means of heaters and fans. Arrangements are usually made so that the temperature cannot rise above a predetermined point, usually fixed at approximately 40°C. When hose is thoroughly dry it should be soft and pliable; if not, it should be returned for further drying.

# 8 Repairing of hose

Immediately hose is returned to a station after use is should be cleaned, tested and carefully examined for damage, careful attention being paid to the smallest signs of abrasions on plastics outer covers. Pinholes and other damage should be marked with indelible pencil immediately they are detected so as to facilitate repair after the hose is dried. It is important that hose is thoroughly dry before repairs are carried out. Hose that is known to have become defective in use is usually rolled up in the reverse way, i.e. with the male coupling inside the female coupling outside. Any lengths which require repair should be set aside and dealt with in accordance with local practice. Some fire brigades have their hose repaired at stations; others arrange for repairs to be carried out at a central depot.

When repairs are done at stations by members of fire brigades, this not only emphasises the necessity for care in handling hose, but also decentralises the amount of repair work to be carried out. The most common damage to hose consist of pinholes; these may be repaired by darning or by patching.

## a. Hose gaiters and bandages

During use holes in hose may be temporarily covered by means of a gaiter or bandage. This will prevent the hose from bursting and will also save water running to waste or damaging property. Several types of gaiter are in use by fire brigades, the most common being the hose bandage. This consists of a 610 mm length of canvas approximately 75 mm in width fitted with a brass eyelet at one end. Lengths of twine are secured to this eyelet and used to lash the bandage in position after it has been wound round the hose over the leak (Fig. 2.11(2)).

Leather gaiters fitted with straps and buckles (Fig. 2.11(1)) may also be used for the same purpose.

A cheap and serviceable gaiter can be made from a piece of discarded 70 mm hose, about 400 mm long, slit up its length, so as to open out, with three brass eyelests (10 mm holes) inserted along one of the short sides. A piece of cord about 610 mm long, knotted centrally to each eyelet, serves to tie the gaiter after it has been bandaged round the hose.

Fig. 2.11 (1) a typical leather hose gaiter. (2) a canvas hose bandage in position on charged hose.

## b. Darning

Hose can be permanently repaired by darning. The equipment required is a bent awl, a needle, a knife and some strands of flax or hemp. The needle should be threaded with four strands of the material and the ends cut level. The operation is carried out in the same way as darning a sock, the hemp or flax being used to re-make the broken strands of the hose.

To replace a broken warp, the weft should be lifted with the awl and the flax or hemp threaded under and over the weft alternately. If more than one strand has to be removed, subsequent strands should be threaded on either side of the first, but where the first strand went under the weft, the second should go over, and so on, so that the pattern of the weave is maintained. If it is necessary to replace both warp and weft, the weft should first be renewed by threading new flax or hemp under and over the warp, and then the warp replaced as described above. When hose has thus been darned, a patch should be affixed over the darn for extra protection.

## c. Patching

Leaks in hose can be satisfactorily repaired by patching if the hose is generally in good condition, and most repairs are now carried out by this method. The patch is applied in a similar manner to that used for repairing motor-car tyre inner tubes. The hose is first carefully cleaned and a prepared patch is then placed over the hole. The hose and patch are then placed in a vulcaniser and heat is applied for the specified time. Special hose vulcanising outfits (Fig. 2.12) are available for the purpose and standard patches are provided.

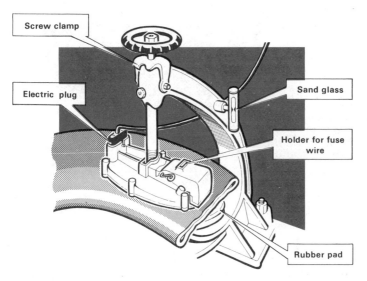

Fig. 2.12 One type of vulcanising outfit, employing electricity for heating. When the correct temperature is reached the fuse wire in the holder melts and breaks the circuit. The sandglass timer is then turned over and when the sand has run through, the clamp is released and the hose is removed.

These patches are not generally suitable for repairing hose manufactured entirely from synthetic materials, and special patches are required for plastics hose; also the temperature needed for vulcanising patches to synthetic hose is somewhat lower than that for conventional hose, while the time required for curing is longer. Manufacturers' instructions should be consulted as to the correct methods, vulcanising temperature, time and type of patch suitable for their particular hose.

When an external patch is applied to lined hose, an additional patch should be affixed internally, otherwise water may get between the lining and the jacket. It is necessary to use a patch carrier for the insertion of internal patches.

Repairs to abrasions on plastics outer covers may be effected without patching. Some manufacturers recommend the use of a special solution which is brushed on with an ordinary paint brush; others recommend the use of heat to melt strips of plastics material into the abraded parts, and the methods and instructions of manufacturers should be carefully followed.

Where a serious burst makes repair by patching impossible, but the remainder of the length of hose is in sufficiently sound condition, the damaged section may be cut out. If it is close to a coupling, then the coupling may be rewired on to the length.

Wherever possible, major repairs to hose should be carried out by specialists. Skilled examination is necessary to detect latent damage, to replace lengths beyond repair and to ensure that appliances are equipped with reliable hose. Damage is varied, often difficult to detect and repair, and skill, experience and equipment are required to carry out efficiently this very important branch of fire equipment maintenance.

## 9 Standard tests

Delivery hose and hose-reel should be tested and examined in accordance with the *Fire Service Drill Book*.

# Chapter 3
# Suction Hose

Suction hose is the name applied to hose designed to resist external pressure. It is used exclusively between the water supply and the pump. As it will withstand internal or external pressure it can be used when working a pump either from open water supplies or from pressure-fed mains. It is an essential part of the equipment of every pumping appliance.

The amount of suction hose normally carried on appliances is about 9 m made up generally in lengths of 2·4 or 3·0 m according to the stowage space available. The diameter of the hose must be such to enable the pump with which it is used to operate at maximum capacity according to the rated output of the pump. The three standard sizes in general use for fire-fighting appliances are 75, 100 and 140 mm diameter, the latter two being widely used on appliances having built-in pumps. The 75mm diameter is mainly used with the smaller capacity portable pumps.

## 1 Construction

Although the lengths and diameters of suction hose vary with the appliances on which it is carried, the construction is substantially the same in every case. The principal feature is that it should possess sufficient strength to withstand without collapsing the pressure of the external air when a vacuum has been created inside; it should also be strong enough to resist the maximum hydrant pressure normally encountered, and at the same time possess the maximum of lightness and flexibility compatible with this strength.

The nominal length of each hose is the length measured over the couplings after they have been fitted. The bore is the nominal diameter with a tolerance of usually + or − 1·6 mm. This is a requirement of the suction hose specification JCDD/2.

Two main types of suction hose are in general use by fire brigades. As with all JCDD specifications, that for suction hose deals with requirements and does not specify any method of manufacture. Therefore either type may be made to the specification according to the purchaser's choice.

## a. Partially-embedded suction hose

This (Fig. 3.1) is usually built up from a tough rubber lining in which is partially embedded a spiral made from tempered galvanised steel wire. The embedding of this internal wire is so arranged as to provide a full waterway and a relatively smooth internal surface.

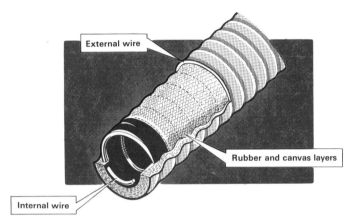

Fig. 3.1 Cutaway view of partially-embedded suction hose.

The wall of the hose is built up from several layers of canvas and rubber into which is embedded wire of similar material to the internal wire. The two spirals are so arranged that each turn of one lies midway between two turns of the other. The complete wall is consolidated by vulcanising.

## b. Smooth-bore suction hose

Smooth bore, or full-embedded suction hose (Fig. 3.2), has a thick internal rubber lining in which a spiral wire is fully embedded. The wall is then built up in the normal manner with plies of fabric and rubber, as for the partially-embedded type.

An advantage of the smooth bore suction hose is that the internal surface offers less resistance to the flow of water than the partially-embedded type. The capacity of a smooth bore hose may be as much as 25 per cent more than that of a hose of partially-embedded construction, and this of course becomes significant at high rates of flow. Another advantage is that the spiral wire cannot be forced from its channel as is sometimes likely when partially-embedded hose is subjected to high internal pressure. The pressure required to force this wire out of position

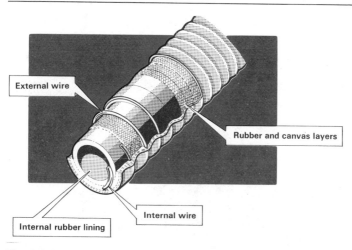

Fig. 3.2 Smooth bore, or fully-embedded, suction hose.

is upwards of 10·5 bar. However, as pressures of this order are not usual, and as hard suction is not widely used when working from hydrants, the disadvantage is not important unless the hose is to be generally used from high pressure hydrants.

The reason more smooth bore suction is not in current use is that it presents certain manufacturing difficulties. It is not easy to make it as flexible as partially-embedded hose, and it is a problem to ensure that the smooth lining will not tend to separate from the body of the hose. This can lead to the collapse of the lining under vacuum causing complete obstruction of the hose. As a check on the lining adhesion, one of the acceptance tests in Specification JCDD/2 is a vacuum test carried out with a special inspection window at one end of the hose, and a light at the other. Under this test any lack of adhesion of the lining will be revealed as a blister.

Suction hose is required to operate under high vacuum conditions, and under internal pressures of up to 7 bar when connected direct to a hydrant. Hose made to Specification JCDD/2 must be constructed to withstand a pressure of 10·5 bar but the actual acceptance test pressure is reduced to 7·6 bar so as not to dislodge the internal wire of partially-embedded hose. Internal wires which have been inadvertently displaced can usually be returned to their original positions provided due care is exercised.

Suction hose made from plastics instead of rubber has been manufactured on an experimental basis, but so far no hose of this type has met all the requirements of Specification JCDD/2.

## 2 Care of suction hose

Because of the materials used and the form of construction, the care and maintenance of suction hose is relatively simple. The hose should be washed after use with clean water. The interior of the hose, the coupling threads and the joint washer should be examined, and the coupling nut should be lubricated as required. No dressings should be used which might cause the rubber to perish.

On many modern appliances it is usual to provide special tunnels for the stowage of suction hose. Where, however, the hose is carried externally, it should be protected from damage resulting from men standing on it or clambering over it when mounting the appliance.

Suction couplings should be treated with care as distortion may cause air leaks. The couplings should never be dropped or dragged along the ground, and the correct size of wrench should always be used for tightening the joints if the universal type of wrench (see Fig. 4.10) is not in use.

## 3 Standard tests

Suction hose should be tested and examined in accordance with the *Fire Service Drill Book.*

## 4 Repairs

Once damaged, suction hose is extremely difficult to repair. This can normally only be done in the case of a puncture, which may be mended by the application of a suitable patch.

## 5 Soft suction

For ease of reference the term *soft suction* is used for delivery hose employed on the intake side of a pump. These lengths are coupled to the pump either by means of a collection head or a suitable hose adaptor (see Part 2, 'Hose fittings').

Soft suction can only be used with a pressure-fed supply, since any reduction of the internal pressure below that of the atmosphere would cause the hose to collapse. Where hydrant pressures and flows are good, soft suction is generally used instead of the standard hard suction hose. Being delivery hose it is capable of withstanding considerably higher internal pressures than standard suction hose, which is constructed primarily to withstand external pressure.

The main advantage in the use of soft suction is that delivery hose lines can be kept short; this makes for ease of control by the pump operator. Further advantages are that it is cheap (good parts cut from a condemned length of delivery hose are frequently used), it is easy to run out and convenient to stow on the appliance.

The lengths of soft suction employed depend to a considerable extent on local preference—from 6 to 9 m is very usual. If additional distances have to be covered, lengths of delivery hose are utilised as required, and two or more pressure supplies can be connected to the pump through a collecting head. Some appliances carry two 4·6 m lengths of 90 mm rubber-lined hose specially for use as soft suction.

Construction of soft suction, its fittings, care and maintenance are precisely the same as for ordinary delivery hose.

# Part 2
# Hose fittings

As a result of developments which have taken place since 1938, many of which were initiated during the life of the National Fire Service, complete standardisation of all essential hose fittings used by local authority fire brigades has now been achieved. This Part, however, deals also with some types of hose fitting which, although less widely used today, are still to be found in existence in some works fire brigades and in many fixed fire-fighting installations.

A wide variety of apparatus which can be classified as hose fittings is used by fire brigades and for the sake of clarity they are dealt with in this Part in the following order: couplings; branches and nozzles; branch holders, radial branches and monitors; standpipes, collecting heads and suction hose fittings; breechings, adaptors, miscellaneous hose fittings and ramps.

It is not practicable to give more than a general description of some of the lesser-used items, and detailed descriptions and illustrations have been reserved for equipment which is likely to be found in current use.

*Specifications*

The following specifications are referred to in this Part:

*British Standard 336:  Fire hose, couplings and ancillary equipment.

British Standard 750:  Underground fire hydrants and dimensions of surface box openings.

JCDD/25:  Hose reel branch for fire brigade use.

---

*A metric version of B.S. 336 is in course of preparation. In due course when couplings of the instantaneous or screw types are manufactured to dimensions given by the revised standard, they will be fully interchangeable with those conforming to the present standard in respect of all mating dimensions. Non-critical dimensions will of course be converted to metric sizes and rounded off as appropriate, and for this reason metric equivalents have not been added to B.S. 336 dimensions quoted in this Part.

# Chapter 4
# Couplings

Generally speaking, any metal fitting for joining two lengths of hose together, or any piece of equipment to a length of hose is termed a coupling. Types of coupling used on hose and hose fittings may be divided into two groups consisting firstly of the type where the joint is made by means of a threaded male and female end, and secondly the type which relies upon some form of interlocking joint.

## 1 Delivery hose couplings

At each end of a length of hose are attached metal fittings called hose couplings, which are normally constructed either of a copper alloy or of an aluminium alloy. Plastics couplings with metal inserts have also been introduced for use in special situations, e.g. where pilfering is common.

A complete coupling consists of two fittings, one attached to each end of the hose. With the exception of one particular type of interlocking coupling, these two fittings are named respectively male and female couplings, and the question of whether an outlet or inlet is male or female depends upon the group to which it belongs. All outlets of the threaded coupling type are male and the inlets female, whereas with couplings of the standard instantaneous type, all outlets are female and the inlets male.

Instantaneous couplings are standard throughout fire brigades in the United Kingdom for delivery hose and pump outlets, whilst screwed type couplings are used on suction hose and pump inlets, hydrant outlets and standpipe bases. A variety of interlocking and threaded couplings are used on hose-reel hose.

There are three main types of interlocking hose coupling: the standard instantaneous, the Surelock or bayonet and the hermaphrodite.

### a. Standard instantaneous couplings

A standard instantaneous coupling is in general use by fire brigades throughout the United Kingdom for use on delivery hose and associated connections, and is covered by British Standard 336. All standard instantaneous female hose couplings (Fig. 4.1(2) and (4)) are fitted with two pull-release spring-loaded plungers (Fig.

4.2), while standard female couplings on pump and standpipe outlets are fitted with a single twist-release spring-loaded plunger (Fig. 4.3).

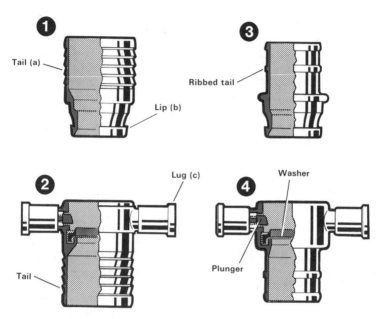

Fig. 4.1 Standard instantaneous hose couplings: (1) male, with multi-serrated tail; (2) female, with multi-serrated tail; (3) male, with ribbed tail; (4) female, with ribbed tail.

British Standard 336 provides for two different types of coupling tailpiece, both of which are in general use. Fig. 4.1(1) and (2) illustrate multi-serrated type tailpieces, while Fig. 4.1(3) and (4) show ribbed-type tailpieces.

The standard male instantaneous coupling is a single metal casting with a tail (Fig. 4.1(a)) for tying it into the hose. The other end of the coupling has an annular lip (b) which engages with the plungers in the female coupling. The female coupling is a metal casting with a tail similar to that of the male. Two hollow lugs (c) are in diametrically opposite positions on either side of the casting. Each lug (Fig. 4.2) is fitted with a spring-loaded plunger (a) which has a cam-shaped tooth (b) for gripping the lip of the male coupling. The top of the plunger is threaded to take a stop nut (c) which holds the cap (d) in position. The cap is circular in shape having externally an enlarged knurled rim at the top to give purchase. It is bored out to fit over the lug, which is

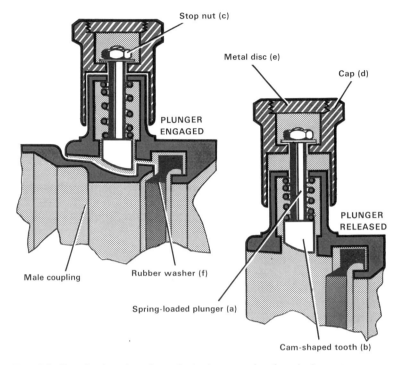

Fig. 4.2 Sketch showing the principal parts of a female instantaneous coupling.

shaped to form a guide through which the shank of the plunger passes, and by which the spring is retained and the tension governed, leaving the cap free to swivel.

A metal disc (e) is fitted into the head of the cap to protect the working parts, provided a closed top. This disc can either be threaded and screwed into the cap or a plain one retained by a circlip. The whole assembly is kept in place by the stop nut, access to which is gained by removing the metal disc from the cap.

When hose fitted with instantaneous couplings is run out, the female coupling is taken towards the fire and the male to the pump or hydrant. Hose which has been rolled round the female coupling is laid out by grasping one lug in each hand (see Fig. 2.6) when the coupling will rotate in the lugs and allow the hose to unwind.

Instantaneous couplings are connected by insertion of the male, the lip of which presses back the two plungers in the female until they are forced into position behind the rim by action of the springs. The watertightness of the joint depends on the action of a specially shaped rubber washer (Fig. 4.2(f)). The water pressure acting on the washer forces it against the tapered tip of the male oupling and against the seating of the female coupling. Should a leak develop at a coupling due to a faulty washer, this can only be remedied by replacing the washer. The couplings are released by seizing the caps on the female coupling and pulling them outwards; this action withdraws the plungers and allows the male coupling to be withdrawn.

When a line of hose is charged, it is extremely difficult to break an instantaneous coupling joint because the water pressure holds the lip of the male coupling securely against the tip of the plunger. It is, therefore, normally necessary to reduce water pressure before attempting to break a coupling joint. Occasions may, however, arise when a speedy disconnection is vital, and in such an emergency when there is no time to reduce pressure, the best action to take is to cut the hose with an axe as near to a coupling as possible.

A single-lug pressure-release type of coupling is fitted to pump and standpipe outlets to permit coupling connections to be instantly broken without the necessity of first reducing water pressure. These couplings have a single-lug twist-release instantaneous connector in which the plunger is raised by a cam action when the cap is twisted. One example of this twist-release mechanism is shown in Fig. 4.3, while in another design small rollers are fitted to follow the cam.

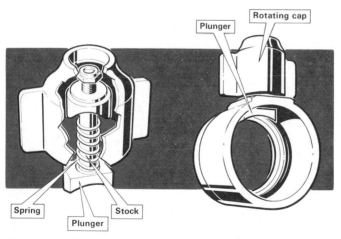

Fig. 4.3 Sketch showing the principal parts of a pressure-release coupling.

In order to permit maximum operational flexibility, all standard instantaneous hose couplings have identical connecting parts irrespective of the size of hose to which they are connected (Fig. 4.4).

Couplings are supplied with a standard range of tailpiece sizes to fit the various types of hose in current use. Thus, two lengths of hose of different sizes may be connected without the use of special adaptors. For example, the standard coupling for use with 90 mm hose has a proportionately larger tailpiece than the coupling used in 45 mm hose, but the marrying parts of both couplings are standard size. It has been found in practice that no significant losses are caused due to restriction of the bore by using the standard coupling with 90 mm hose.

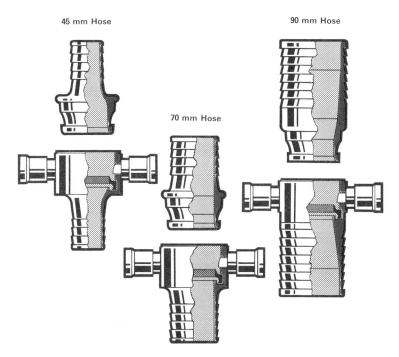

Fig. 4.4 Standard instantaneous hose couplings for attachment to hose of different diameters.

## b. 'Surelock' or bayonet couplings

While this type of coupling is not widely used by fire brigades, it may be found in use on some fireboats and sometimes on radial branches. The male coupling (Fig. 4.5(1)), is a metal casting with

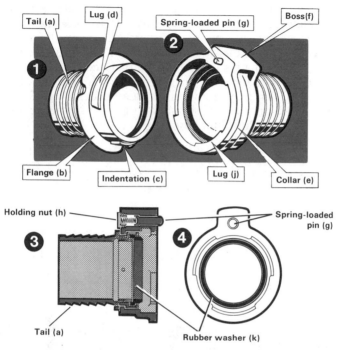

Fig. 4.5 'Surelock' or bayonet couplings: (1) male coupling; (2, 3 and 4) female coupling.

a tail (a) having external serrations for attaching the hose by wired ties. Near the other end is a wide flange (b) with three regularly-spaced semicircular indentations (c) in its outer periphery, opposite which are three lugs (d).

The female coupling (Fig. 4.5(2, 3 and 4)) is a metal casting with a tail similar to that of the male. A heavy collar (e), slightly stepped back in two steps towards the tail, is fitted at the non-serrated end. On one side of this collar, formed in the casting, is a squared boss (f) protruding from the collar. This boss has a spring-loaded pin (g) running parallel with the coupling and held in position by a holding nut (h) with its head towards the shank end. Inside the orifice of the coupling are three equidistant lugs (j) and a rubber washer (k).

On connecting the couplings, the male is inserted in the female so that the internal bosses of the latter engage with the external ones of the former, and the male is turned until the spring-loaded pin is free to move into one of the indentations on the male flange. The couplings are released by pressing the pin in against the spring and giving the male a partial turn.

## c. Hermaphrodite couplings

This type of interlocking coupling is still used for delivery hose, but is normally only encountered at docks and on board ships. As its name implies, both parts of the coupling (Fig. 4.6) are identical, and it is the one case where reference to male and

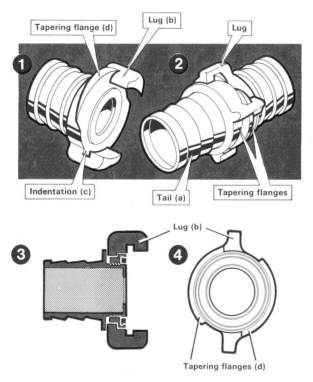

Fig. 4.6 Hermaphrodite couplings: (1) half coupling: (2) two half-couplings joined; (3 and 4) section and end view of the coupling.

female couplings cannot be applied. Each part consists of a metal casting with an external serrated tail (a) for wiring on the hose, terminating in a collar slightly over 25 mm in depth. On this collar are two diametrically opposite lugs (b), extending beyond the orifice. A squared indentation (c) is cut on the inside of this extension to engage two tapering flanges (d), each commencing at one lug and ending some 50 mm short of the other.

To connect hose by means of this coupling, the two parts are put together so that the lugs of each pass through the gaps between the lugs and the flanges of the other. A partial turn of one section then locks the coupling. One disadvantage of this type of coupling is the danger of leakage at the joint because there is no positive lock, and a tendency for the coupling to work loose. An advantage is that, being an hermaphrodite coupling, it is immaterial which end of a length of hose is run out towards the fire.

It is not uncommon for fire brigades covering waterfront and shipping risks to carry supplies of adaptors to enable hermaphrodite couplings to be connected to standard fire brigade couplings.

## 2 Hose-reel couplings

Couplings for use on hose-reel hose are not standardised in the fire service and various types are used, the most common being various patterns of the screw and hermaphrodite type. The couplings are normally made of gunmetal or hot brass pressings.

Fig. 4.7(2), shows one example of a simple screw-type threaded

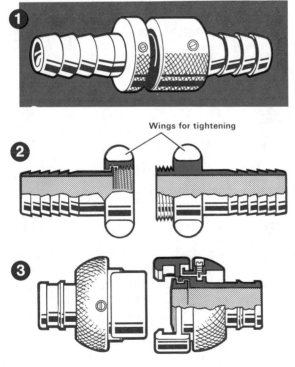

Fig. 4.7 Hose-reel couplings: (1) and (2) screwed types; (3) hermaphrodite type.

hose-reel coupling with wings for finger and thumb tightening. Fig. 4.7(1), illustrates a more modern type of threaded hose-reel coupling, which is tightened by the use of two 'C' spanners. The coupling illustrated in Fig. 4.7(3), is an example of a modern hermaphrodite coupling which is used by many brigades.

Experiments have been carried out with hose-reel couplings of coiled-spring/nylon construction, but couplings of this type are not at present likely to be found in many brigades.

## 3 Screw-type couplings

Although they are not now used by fire brigades, couplings of the screw-thread type may be found in some places e.g. on fixed fire-fighting installations. Two types of thread were commonly

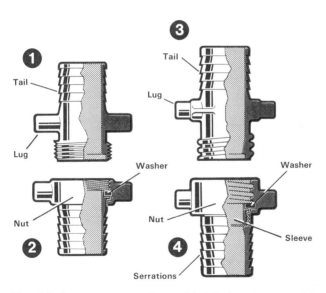

Fig. 4.8 Screw-type couplings: (1) 'V' thread, male; (2) 'V' thread, female; (3) round-thread, male; (4) round-thread, female.

used in the manufacture of these couplings and examples of 'round' and 'V' thread couplings are shown in Fig. 4.8. These couplings have to be tightened with the aid of spanners designed to fit over the coupling lugs.

## 4 Suction hose couplings and wrenches

### a. Couplings

For normal fire brigade fire-fighting pumps, round-threaded suction couplings either 100 or 140 mm diameter are used in accordance with B.S. 336, which also covers 75 and 125 mm diameter sizes. Suction couplings of other sizes, some having 'V' threads, are to be found on small pumps, such as those used by contractors, and sometimes by fire brigades for various small pumping out jobs.

The standard male coupling for suction hose (Fig. 4.9(1)) has a two-ribbed tail (a), two fixed lugs (b) and a threaded end (c). The female coupling (Fig. 4.9(2)) consists of three castings: tail (a),

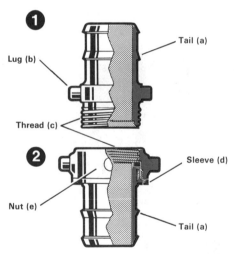

Fig. 4.9 Suction couplings: (1) male coupling; (2) female coupling.

sleeve (d) and nut (e). These are assembled in the same manner as the female round-thread delivery hose coupling. The nut has four lugs as against the two on the male, and the threaded end of the male coupling is slightly enlarged internally to seat against a leather or composition washer in the female. Some suction hose couplings will be found to have multi-serrated tails instead of the ribbed tails illustrated in Fig. 4.9.

Suction hose coupling threads should be kept lightly greased; a graphite grease is very suitable, but if rubber washers are used, the grease must not be allowed to come into contact with them and so cause deterioration.

Since a leak, however small, in suction couplings will allow air to enter and make it difficult or impossible to obtain the necessary pressure drop to lift water, particular care in their maintenance is essential. They should never be dropped or roughly handled in such a way as to distort them, and when joined together they must be tightened by using two suction wrenches, one on either coupling.

### b. Suction coupling wrenches

There are two types of suction wrench in general use by fire brigades. The earlier conventional type (Fig. 4.10(1)) is made in

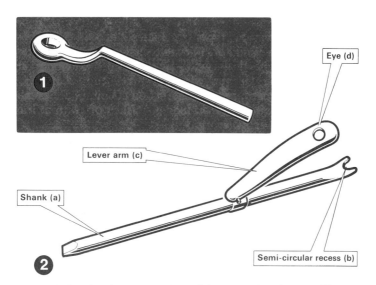

Fig. 4.10 Suction hose wrenches: (1) conventional type; (2) universal type.

different sizes to fit the various sizes of suction hose coupling, and consists of a short length of steel bar, one end of which is beaten flat and shaped into an arc to fit the particular size of coupling on which it is to be used. An eye is provided at the shaped end for engaging one of the coupling lugs, and when used the curve of the wrench should follow the curve of the coupling.

A later type of suction wrench is the universal type (Fig. 4.10(2)), which is designed to fit any size of suction coupling. It consists of a tubular steel shank (a) with one end flattened, slightly curved and shaped at the end in a semi-circular recess (b). A reinforced strip steel lever arm (c) is pivoted to the bar about 180 mm from the bottom end. The lever arm is also slightly curved and has an elliptical shaped eye (d) about 25 mm from its end.

The eye in the lever arm is placed over one of the coupling lugs while the semi-circular recess at the end of the bar is placed firmly against the opposite lug, thus enabling pressure to be applied to tighten the joint.

## 5 Method of securing hose to couplings

The standard method of securing hose to delivery and suction hose couplings which have externally serrated and ribbed type tails is by binding the hose on to the tail with copper or galvanised mild steel wire. This is done by means of a hose coupling binder of which there are various types (see Plates 7 and 8). Some hose coupling binders have adaptors to enable suction as well as delivery hose couplings to be dealt with. Delivery hose couplings are usually tied in with 1·6 mm wire, the wire being tied over a protective guard of canvas webbing. Suction couplings are usually tied in with 2 mm wire and the binding finished off with at least one run of solder over its length.

One type of hose binder is illustrated in Fig. 4.11; the method of binding described can be regarded as representative of current practice. A fixed threaded supporting spindle (a) attached to a bracket screwed to a bench has at its outer end a plate with a holed anchoring pin (b). On the outer side of this plate is an interchangeable adaptor (c) to which the coupling is fitted. The hose to be attached is supported on an X-shaped wooden crutch (Fig. 4.11(2)), and a piece of canvas or sometimes leather, is laid around it where the binding will fall, to protect the hose from damage by the wire. The whole of the apparatus except the plate and adaptor revolves around a threaded pivot (d) on the spindle. From the spool of wire (e) the free end is led under tension beneath the guide wheel (f) and grooved guide (g) over the coupling, and is threaded through the eye of the anchoring pin (b).

Fig. 4.11 (opposite) Hose coupling binder: (1) general view; (2 to 7) stages in the binding process.

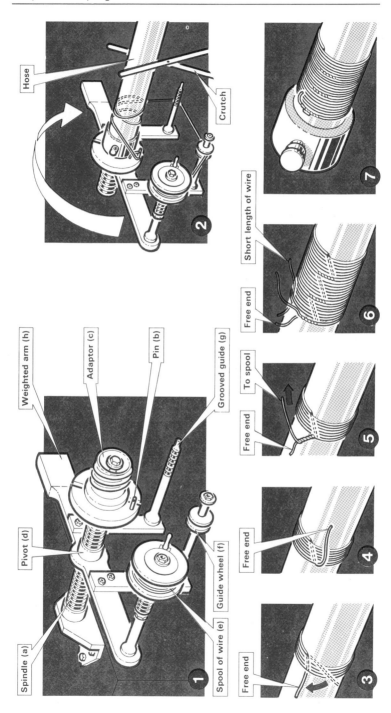

Weighted arm (h)

Adaptor (c)

Pin (b)

Grooved guide (g)

Hose

Crutch

Pivot (d)

Spindle (a)

Guide wheel (f)

Spool of wire (e)

Short length of wire

Free end

Free end

To spool

Free end

Free end

Free end

47

Standing on the right, the operator puts on a turn by swinging round in a clockwise direction the weighted arm (h) which has been moved to the adaptor end of the threaded spindle. This turn is adjusted so that the second turn, the first of the binding proper, will come just inside the extreme serration on the tail of the coupling. The second comes over the first turn (Fig. 4.11(2)), as do those that follow, the pivot travelling down the thread as the turns are made.

In the case of the multi-serrated tailpiece, when four turns have been put on (Fig. 4.11(3)), the free end of the binding wire is removed from the anchoring pin and pulled up towards the operator, and the binding is continued over it as before. After the eighth turn (4) the free end is pulled over, hammered against the binding and held. The tension is eased and the binding tied in by twisting it three times with the free end (5). The twists are pulled tight with pliers, the tension reapplied, the tie bedded home with hammer and blunt chisel and binding continued until the sixteenth turn; the binding is again tied in. A short length of wire is placed under the twenty-first and subsequent turns (6). The binding is finished on the twenty-fourth turn and tied in. The wire to the spool is cut, its end flattened, the short length of wire pulled out and the wire with the flattened end inserted in its place, turned back, cut off, and its end hammered well down. The free end is then turned back on its tie and its end hammered down (7).

Instantaneous couplings have to be prevented from rotating in the adaptor during binding; in the case of the female, this is done by a long bolt attached to the adaptor plate, which engages the lug of the coupling; in the case of the male, movement is prevented by leaving the free end of the binding wire attached to the anchoring pin throughout the whole binding process, ties being made with a false tie wire. The final tie is made with this wire, and the binding finished off as before; the free end is then removed from the anchoring pin, cut off, turned over the binding, and hammered down.

With any form of binding, the method of gripping the coupling is important. This is especially so in the case of the male instantaneous coupling. As it is liable to distortion, it should be gripped from the inside by a device such as an expanding mandrel. On no account should an external vice be employed.

In the case of the two-ribbed tailpiece, this is usually secured by two separate ties of not less than five turns each. With suction hose, which is usually supplied complete with couplings, binding continues for a minimum of 108 mm in the case of 100 mm hose, and a minimum of 133 mm for 140 mm hose. Hose reel couplings are often bound in with wire although other methods are used, including swaging them in by means of a metal collar which is fitted with a tool called a ring presser.

# Chapter 5
# Branches and nozzles

The branchpipe, or 'branch' as it is generally called, is used at the delivery end of a line of hose to increase the velocity of the water as it approaches the nozzle, and so provide an effective fire-fighting jet. The size of the jet is governed by the nozzle, which screws on to the outlet end of the branch. The branch consists of a metal tube having an internal diameter which reduces gradually in size towards the delivery end. The reduction in area is further continued in the nozzle until at the orifice the diameter measurement is that by which the nozzle and jet are known. Branchpipe and nozzle connections are standardised in accordance with BS 336.

Branches may be divided into three principal classes:

(1) Those that yield a fire stream in the form of a jet which cannot be controlled by the branch operator.

(2) Those that provide for some form of control by shutting off the jet, altering its shape or size, or changing its character, e.g. converting it into a spray.

(3) Those which are used exclusively on hose-reel hose.

## 1 Branches without control facilities

### a. Standard branches

These branches, which are standard in every respect except length, are normally made of alloys of copper or aluminium and have at the inlet end a standard male instantaneous coupling for connection to a female instantaneous delivery hose coupling. The outlet end terminates in a male 45 mm BSP thread, 11 threads per 25 mm, for connecting to the female thread of the standard nozzle. A washer, usually of synthetic rubber or leather, is used for making a watertight joint between nozzle and branch.

The internal bore of the branch is of smooth finish and tapers gradually from a diameter of about 65 mm at the inlet orifice to about 45 mm at the outlet orifice to which the nozzle is connected. BS 336 specifies a minimum length of 200 mm for the body of the branch, but this may be increased if so required by the purchaser.

Fig. 5.1(1) illustrates a standard type branch with an instantaneous male connection at the inlet end and a standard 'V' thread at the nozzle end.

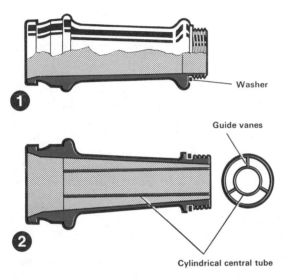

Fig. 5.1 Branches without control facilities: (1) a standard branch; (2) a 'streamform' branch.

## b. Non-standard branches

In the nineteenth century, branches were often as much as $1 \cdot 8$m in length and they had various patterns of screw-type connections at the inlet end. The outlet often took the form of a fixed nozzle which was in fact an integral part of the branch. Because of weight considerations, these long branches were constructed of comparatively thin metal (usually copper) and they were easily dented and damaged. Non-standard branches of various patterns may still be encountered, usually on fixed installations in the older type of factory, hotel and similar premises, and they may be found to have old-type screw connections to match whatever type of hose coupling which happens to be in use on the premises. Non-standard branches of this kind are not used nowadays by fire brigades.

One type of non-standard branch which is still used by some fire brigades is known as the 'streamform' branch (Fig. 5.1(2)). In outward appearance it is similar to the standard branch, but is fitted internally throughout its whole length with a cylindrical tube of equal diameter throughout, held in position by three longitudinal guide vanes. It is claimed that this type of branch reduces turbulent effects and thus produces a more solid jet.

Experiments have been carried out with branches and nozzles made of plastic mouldings and other synthetic materials, but although they are used to some extent on the Continent, they have not so far gained general favour in this country. Another type of lightweight branch which has been produced and used experimentally is one with a fixed nozzle which is an integral part of the branch casting, but it has not so far been adopted for general use by fire brigades.

## 2 Branches with control facilities

There are many different patterns of hand-controlled branch in common use by fire brigades, all designed to enable branchmen to control or change in one way or another the formation of the water stream by the operation of either levers, triggers or various forms of threaded attachment. With most hand-controlled branches, the branchman can change the pattern of the water stream from a jet to a diffused spray, or vice versa, or stop the flow altogether.

### a. The hand-controlled branch

One example of a hand-controlled branch is illustrated in Fig. 5.2, and this particular pattern can be adjusted so that either a jet or spray, or both, can be obtained, each being independently controllable by the branchman. The spray may, within certain limits, be adjusted to any desired angle and may be used as a protection against heat and smoke, while at the same time a solid jet is available with which to attack the heart of the fire.

Below the base of the detachable nozzle is a rotating collar (a), fitted with lugs, which controls the spray; approximately halfway down the casting a semi-circular handle (b) controls the jet. In its essentials the hand-controlled branch consists of an inner tube (c) communicating direct with the nozzle, governed by a jet valve (d) operated by the semicircular handle, and the annular space between the inner tube and the main casting communicating with the spray outlet, which is opened or closed by rotating the movable collar on a screw thread, the adjustment of which controls the angle of the spray. The nozzle is screwed to the branch in conventional manner, but the internal dimensions of the branch do not allow for the use of nozzles larger than 22 mm diameter.

When the jet handle (b) is in the forward position (Fig. 5.2(1)), the entrance to the inner tube is closed. When the handle is pulled back (Fig. 5.2(2)) the bore in the valve allows water to pass through into the tube and on through the nozzle from which it

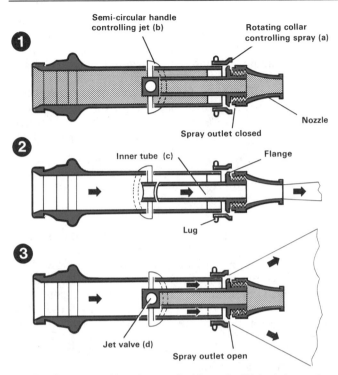

Fig. 5.2 One type of hand-controlled branch: (1) both jet and spray shut; (2) jet open, spray shut; (3) jet shut, spray open.

emerges in jet form. The supply of water to the spray outlet is independent of the jet valve which it bypasses to enter the cavity between the inner tube and the outer casing of the branch. Operation of the spray control collar (a) in a clockwise direction (when looking towards the nozzle orifice) presses it tightly against the flange on the branch outlet and shuts off the spray. When turned in an anti-clockwise direction (Fig. 5.2(3)), water flows in the form of a spray, the angle of which is controlled by the amount by which the control collar is turned. The spray can be varied from a cone of about 30 to 40 degrees to a flat sheet of 180 degrees. When changing over from jet to spray, the spray should always be turned on *before* the jet is shut off in order to minimise the sudden build-up of pressure along the hose line.

Another type of hand-controlled branch is illustrated in Fig. 5.3, in which a floating rotary valve enables the operator to adjust the water stream to give either a straight jet, a fine or coarse spray, or a complete shut-off. With this type of hand-controlled branch, the spray nozzle can be extended on the end of an extension piece or applicator for use on oil or similar fires.

With any type of hand-controlled branch, great care must always be taken in the way the hand controls are operated, particularly when shutting off, which must always be done gradually. Careless use of a hand-controlled branch can easily cause serious damage to hose and be a source of danger to the branchman and others in the vicinity.

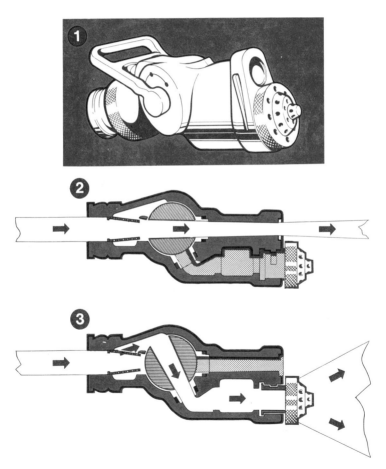

Fig. 5.3 Another type of hand-controlled branch: (1) general view; (2) operation of the jet; (3) operation of the spray.

## b. Diffuser branch

Another type of branch with control facilities which is used by many brigades is illustrated in Fig. 5.4(1). It was first introduced during the life of the National Fire Service; it is known as a diffuser branch and consists of a main body in which is rigidly

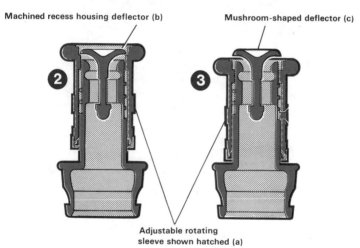

**Machined recess housing deflector (b)**      **Mushroom-shaped deflector (c)**

**Adjustable rotating
sleeve shown hatched (a)**

Fig. 5.4 Diffuser branch: (1) general view; (2) sectional view with the branch fully closed; (3) sectional view with the branch fully open giving a 180 degrees spray.

mounted a mushroom-shaped deflector, and a male instantaneous coupling for connection to the hose. A rotating sleeve (a) with a milled grip travels in a coarse thread screw. At the forward end of the sleeve is a machined recess (b) somewhat wider in diameter than the head of the deflector (c). As the sleeve is moved forward this recess envelops the head of the deflector, leaving an annular opening which is gradually reduced as the sleeve moves forward, until it is closed off when the sleeve reaches the full extent of its travel. When the sleeve is fully withdrawn a flat spray (180 degrees) is produced, whilst as it is moved forward the angle of spray is progressively reduced owing to the directing effect of the recess.

This type of diffuser can be adjusted to give either a useful fire stream or a diffused spray of adjustable intensity (see Plates 9 and 10), which varies from an intense mist over an angle of 180 degrees (Fig. 5.4(3)) to a complete shut-off (Fig. 5.4(2)). For smoke driving, or for cooling the atmosphere in a room, the best adjustment is when the spray forms an angle of about 90 degrees. If a liquid (Class 'B') fire is to be attacked, the angle of spray should be closed down to about 30 degrees to give a very dense or concentrated spray. This type of spray is also very useful for attacking fires of ordinary free-burning material at close quarters, e.g. inside a room. If circumstances prevent close approach to the fire, the spray angle can be closed down until a moderately good fire stream or straight jet is produced, and for small fires where the use of large quantities of water is undesirable, or where only a small quantity of water is available, the jet can be reduced still further until it is comparable with the size of a hose-reel jet.

It has been found by experiment that the best results are obtained if the branch pressure is maintained at 5·5 to 7 bar although quite good results are obtainable with pressures as low as 3·5 bar. The approximate amount of water discharged in litres per minute at various adjustments through this diffuser branch is given in Table 1.

## Table 1

| Pressure in bars | Litres per minute | | | |
| --- | --- | --- | --- | --- |
| | Wide spray 90 deg. | Narrow spray 30 deg. | Fire stream | Hose-reel stream |
| 7 | 640 | 550 | 310 | |
| 6 | 605 | 490 | 215 | 40 |
| 5 | 565 | 430 | 150 | to |
| 4 | 520 | 370 | 105 | 70 |
| 3 | 470 | 310 | – | |

Care must be taken to ensure that there is no obstruction in the orifice between the deflector and the nozzle, otherwise poor streams or spray will result. Branches should be examined after use and any obstruction removed.

## 3 Hose-reel branches

The simplest type of hose-reel branch likely to be encountered takes the form of a pet-cock similar to the one illustrated in Fig. 5.5(1) in which the jet can be turned on and off by means of a rotating valve. Many branches of this type are to be found on fixed hose-reel installations in factories and places of public entertainment. The diameter of the nozzle outlet is normally either 5 or 6 mm and the nozzle orifice is sometimes protected by a rubber ring.

Most fire brigades now use more modern types of hose-reel branch which have the dual purpose function of providing either a straight jet or alternatively a spray which can be adjusted by the operator to give a dense mist of fine intensity or a coarse spray. With most models both jet and spray can be used simultaneously when required. One example of a dual-purpose hose-reel branch is illustrated in Fig. 5.5(2). It is manufactured in a light alloy and has two outlets, one fitted with a 5 mm nozzle for normal hose-reel jet work, and the other with a specially designed dome-shaped spray head 50 mm in diameter. This particular spray head operates best at pressures between 7 to 8 bar but satisfactory results can be obtained at pressures down to 5·5 bar. A 1·8 m extension piece (in two 1 metre) lengths is provided for use when necessary between the branch and the spray head to enable spray to be applied into inaccessible places. Other examples of different types of hose-reel branch which are in current use are illustrated in Fig. 5.5(3, 4 and 5).

A specification (JCDD/25)—'Hose reel branch for fire brigade use' has been prepared by the Joint Committee on Design and Development of Appliances and Equipment of the Central Fire Brigades Advisory Councils and has been issued by the Home Office and the Scottish Home and Health Department. It relates to a jet/spray branch capable of being used on appliances at a pressure of 10·5 bar or more. The branch should be designed as a trigger-operated gun with a pistol grip and should preferably have a forward grip to assist in steadying and aiming the gun. The forward grip should also serve as a jet/spray control. The performance at 7 bar is required to comply with one of the rates of flow as shown in Table 2. The method of measuring the throw is detailed in an appendix to the specification.

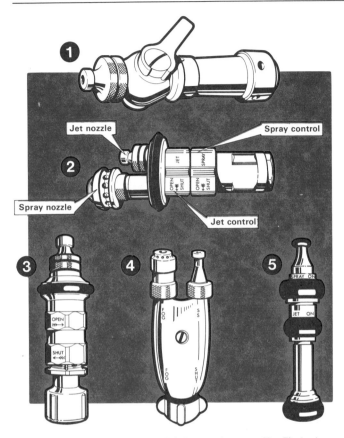

Fig. 5.5 Hose reel branches: (1) Pet-cock type; (2—5) dual-purpose jet/ spray types.

## Table 2

| Rate of flow per minute | Jet or narrow angle spray of not more than 5 deg. Throw not less than | Spray with cone angle not less than 40 deg.* Throw not less than |
|---|---|---|
| litres | metres | metres |
| 54·0 | 10·7 | 6·1 |
| 68.0 | 10·7 | 6·4 |
| 91·0 | 10·7 | 7·6 |

*The spray should be uniformly distributed throughout the cone angle.

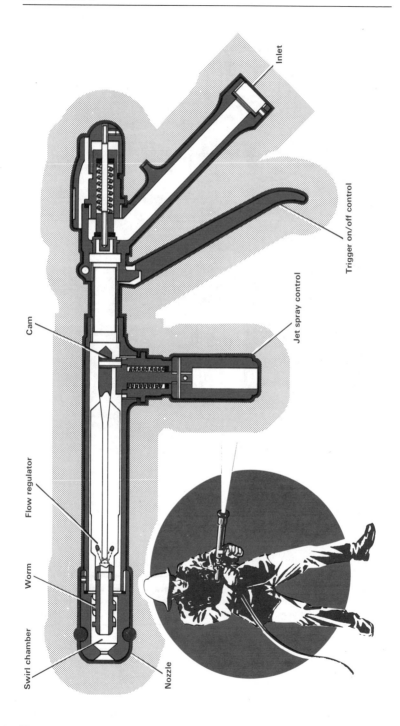

Inlet

Trigger on/off control

Jet spray control

Cam

Flow regulator

Worm

Swirl chamber

Nozzle

A pistol-type hose-reel which conforms to the specification is shown in Fig. 5.6. It is made of aluminium alloy, corrosive-resistant steel and nylon and weighs about 900 g. The on/off control is provided by the trigger and the jet/spray control is located beneath the barrel. When the flow regulator and worm are in the position shown in the diagram, water passes through the worm in the annular chamber surrounding the flow regulator, passes through the swirl chamber and emerges from the nozzle in the form of a finely atomised spray. When a jet is required, the flow regulator is moved forward under the action of the control cam and the water is then directed towards the nozzle via the centre passage in the flow regulator, by-passing the swirl chamber.

This type of branch is also suitable for use with high pressure hose-reel pumps, such as the Godiva UMP (see the *Manual, Part 2: Chapter 1, 'Pumps, primers and pumping appliances'*).

## 4 Nozzles

### a. Standard nozzles

Nozzles (Fig. 5.7(1)) to fit standard branches are normally made of alloys of copper or aluminium, and have standard connections in accordance with BS 336. The standard nozzle connection is a female 45 mm BSP thread (11 threads per 25 mm). The internal surface of the nozzle is smooth and at the branch end is of the same internal diameter as the delivery orifice of the branch. The bore is shaped to give the best hydraulic conditions and the nozzle orifice is recessed slightly to protect the rim from damage.

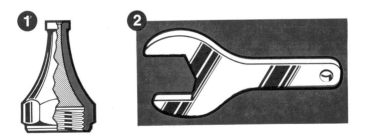

Fig. 5.7 (1) a standard nozzle. (2) nozzle spanner.

Fig. 5.6 (opposite) A pistol-type hose-reel branch conforming to specification JCDD/25.

Externally, a solid rim adds further protection to the nozzle orifice.

The edge of the nozzle orifice should be free from scratches or indentations and the internal surface should be perfectly smooth because the smallest defect will cause the jet to break up and thus impair its efficiency. At the branch end, the base of the nozzle is hexagonally shaped to permit the use of a spanner (Fig. 5.7(2)),when necessary, although a hand-tight joint is usually sufficient provided the washer is in good condition. Excessive force should not be used to tighten the nozzle as this may damage the washer and cause leakage.

For normal use on standard branches, nozzles are made in a range of sizes from 5 mm outlet to 25 or 29 mm while larger sizes to fit special branches are made for use on monitors and radial branches.

The term 'working nozzle' is used for a nozzle normally attached to the branch which is first used when getting to work at a fire. The size adopted for working nozzles is usually 19 mm or less, but this varies with local preference after consideration of such factors as the type of risk normally involved. For fires in ships, working nozzles are generally restricted to 13 or 16 mm.

## b. Hose-reel nozzles

As can be seen from the description of hose-reel branches on pages 56 to 59 (which for convenience also includes hose-reel nozzles), there are various types of hose-reel nozzle and spray head in use by fire brigades. Hose-reel nozzles normally have either a 5 or 6 mm jet orifice, and those which are detachable are usually screwed to the branch by means of a standard BSP thread.

Hose-reel spray heads are usually detachable and in some cases are designed so that they may be used on the end of extension tubes (sometimes called 'applicators'), which can be attached to the branch to enable spray to be applied in inaccessible places.

## c. Small nozzles

A variety of patterns of small nozzle are used on such appliances as hand pumps, stirrup pumps and portable extinguishers. They are usually designed to produce a jet and may or may not have a control cock. Some, however, are of a dual-purpose nature with simple control facilities to enable the operator to adjust the nozzle to produce either a jet or a diffused spray.

# 5 Special types of branch and nozzle

A considerable number of unconventional nozzles and branches were at one time used by fire brigades and although rarely used nowadays, some may still be found in existence. Some of them were of general manufacture whilst others were made up locally, including types which could be adjusted by the branchman to give a jet of any size from 25 mm to a complete shut-off. Others were designed to produce various grades of spray and were known by such names as spreading nozzles, fan spreaders, globe spreaders and rose nozzles.

Examples of special types of branch and nozzle which are in current use are described and illustrated in the following paragraphs.

## a. Chimney nozzles

One type of chimney nozzle in current use is illustrated in Fig. 5.8(1). It consists of two light alloy metal castings; the dome-shaped head (a) having a number of pairs of small jet orifices (b) recessed around the outer periphery of the casting and set at opposing right-angles so that the jets are directed laterally but at different angles. Screwed into the head is a base casting (c) with a female thread to take the male thread of a chimney rod (d), and a multi-serrated tail (e) to which conventional sized stirrup-pump tubing (f) can be attached.

The smooth dome shape of the nozzle enables it to be easily pushed up inside chimneys by the aid of chimney rods, while a stirrup pump is used to feed the jets which are directed by the nozzle to the internal sides of the chimney.

## b. Basement spray

This is an attachment, suitably threaded for fixing to a branchpipe outlet. It consists of a metal fitting (Fig. 5.8(2)), to which is attached a deflector plate so constructed as to throw a spray of water in all directions in sprinkler head fashion. The basement spray is for use on fires in such places as basements and ships, holds where an all-round cooling effect is required.

## c. Revolving nozzles

Various types of revolving nozzle have from time to time been designed for lowering into cellars, basements and ships' holds,

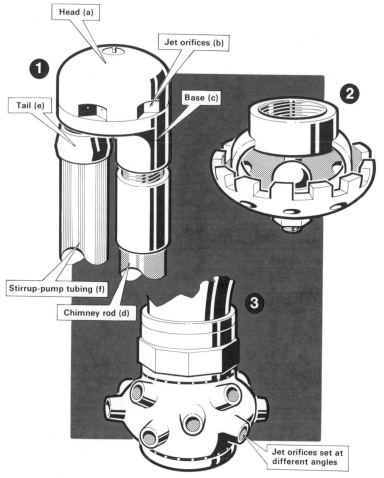

Fig. 5.8 (1) A chimney nozzle. (2) Basement spray for connecting to a branch. (3) A revolving nozzle.

but the two described may be taken as being generally representative. The first one consists of a male instantaneous coupling carrying a semi-spherical metal casting approximately 150 to 200 mm in diameter which is designed to revolve freely in a plane at right angles to the coupling. Fitted to the casting are 5 mm nozzles at right angles to the hose. Each nozzle is inclined to an angle of 45 degrees to the diameter. Two diametrically opposite nozzles throw jets in the plane of revolution whilst, of the other two, one is turned slightly upwards and the other slightly downwards. As water passes under pressure through the branch, it revolves, throwing out a curtain of water in all directions.

Fig. 5.8(3), illustrates a modern type of revolving nozzle which is more compact than the one just described. The nozzle has twelve jet orifices set at different angles, for both rotation and spreading purposes and revolves on ballbearings. This type of revolving nozzle has a standard female nozzle thread to enable it to be attached to any standard branch, and is sufficiently compact to be used for lowering through small apertures, such as a hole cut in a floor or through a ship's ventilator.

### d. Revolving branches

Fig. 5.9 illustrates a double revolving branch, which is made in two parts. The upper part comprises a collecting breeching for two lines of hose which support the casting when in use, andd the lower section, which revolves on ball-bearings, is fitted with four equidistant outlets. Two of of these (diametrically opposite) are in the form of branches to which ordinary standard nozzles may be attached. The other two outlets (the driving nozzles), also located opposite to each other, are inclined to the diameter.The slanting streams of water issuing from these two nozzles develop the jet reaction which causes the lower casting to revolve.

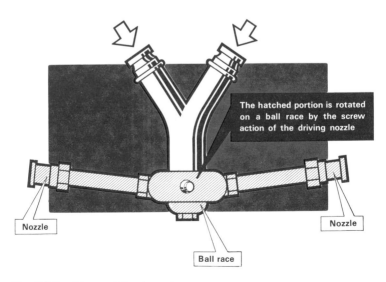

The hatched portion is rotated on a ball race by the screw action of the driving nozzle

Nozzle

Nozzle

Ball race

Fig. 5.9 Double revolving branch.

Other types have a single instantaneous inlet fitted with two jets for rotation and with two streamform branches to project the water, or three nozzles set at different angles which serve for both rotation and fire fighting.

### e. Cellar pipe

This piece of equipment is designed for use in smoky fires in cellars, basements and sometimes ship fires, and may be actuated either through a hatchway, cellar flap or a hole cut in the floor above. As can be seen from Fig. 5.10, a cellar pipe is coupled to a delivery hose at coupling (a) and held in position by means of

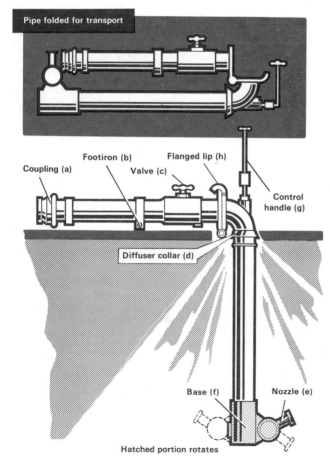

Fig. 5.10 Cellar pipe.

the footiron (b). The flow of water, which can be controlled by the valve (c), is delivered in spray form through a diffuser collar (d) as well as in jet form through a swivel-mounted nozzle (e) attached to a revolving base (f). Movement of the nozzle and base are controlled by use of control handle (g) which, when turned, rotates the base, while vertical movement of the handle directs the swivel-mounted nozzle upwards or downwards. The cellar pipe folds for stowage purposes by means of the joint at (h).

## f. Miscellaneous special branches

'Extended' branches designed for specialised use on such fires as those involving grain, coal and haystacks are occasionally used by some fire brigades and they are usually constructed to meet local requirements. For example, one type of special branch for dealing with fires in coal stacks and bunkers consists of a 3 m length of 65 mm steel piping having at one end a pointed head which is pierced with a number of 3 mm holes and at the other end, a thread on which may be screwed either a collar containing a standard hose coupling, or another 3 m section of piping to extend the branch still farther. A driving head may also be screwed on to this thread to enable the branch to be driven into the stack or bunker, after which the head is withdrawn and the coupling screwed on so that the hose can be connected.

# Chapter 6
# Branch holders, monitors and radial branches

## 1 Branch holders

The purpose of a branch holder is to take either the whole or part of the weight and reaction of a charged branch. Some types are designed purely to assist the branchman to control the branch and direct the jet (Fig. 6.1(1)) and do not obviate the need for

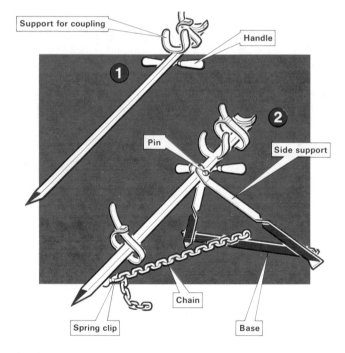

Fig. 6.1 Two types of portable branch holder.

manning the branch. Other types Fig. 6.1(2)) are designed so that they may be placed in position, adjusted to direct the jet in the required trajectory, and then left unattended whilst the branch-man either retires to a place of safety (if the jet has to be got to work from a potentially dangerous position) or carries on with other work.

The delivery end of the hose is laid along the holder with the coupling lugs close against the coupling support, and the branch is then securely strapped in position so that the nozzle protrudes over the end of the branch holder.

## 2 Monitors

Monitors are used in circumstances where very large quantities of water in jet form are required, and they fall broadly into two categories:

(a) portable monitors, which are designed to stand on the ground, and

(b) fixed monitors permanently secured to fire appliances, such as fireboats or fire-fighting tugs, and turntable ladders.

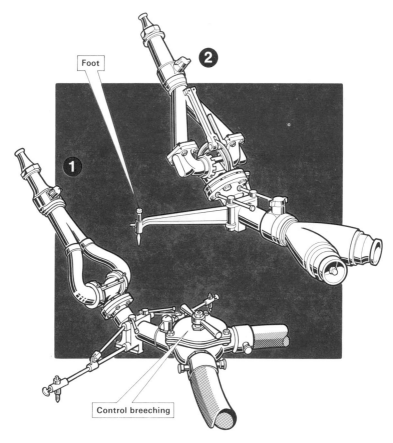

Fig. 6.2 Two types of portable monitor: (1) with control breeching; (2) with two-way collecting breeching.

## a Portable monitors

These are rarely used except on very large fires where copious quantities of water are required or in circumstances when it is necessary to leave a large working jet in a position of danger due, for example, to the risk of falling walls. They may be found with nozzles up to 50–65 mm diameter, and the large quantities of water required are usually fed to the monitor through twin lines of hose terminating in a collecting breeching, which may be a fixture on the monitor although sometimes a separate breeching is used with its outlet connected to the monitor with a short length of 90 mm hose.

Various patterns of portable monitor have from time to time been produced by manufacturers. Most of them have swivelling joints which permit the jet to be directed as required within certain limits, and have legs or feet to hold the apparatus firmly in position on the ground. The portable monitor illustrated in Fig. 6.2(1), is shown connected to a control-type collecting breeching. The one illustrated in Fig. 6.2(2), is shown connected directly to a two-way collecting breeching fitted with mushroom-type non-return valves; it can be collapsed for compact stowage purposes.

Another type of portable monitor was produced by the Home Office, and this is shown in Fig. 6.3.

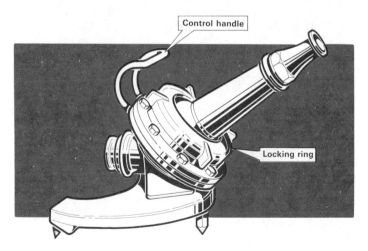

Fig. 6.3 Portable monitor, Home Office type. The branch can be held in the required position by tightening the locking ring.

## b. Fixed monitors

### (1) Fireboats

Monitors on fireboats are almost invariably rigidly connected to the deck and sometimes have permanent piping arrangements from the pumps. They are usually of the 'straight-through' type and, with an unlimited supply of water, can deliver up to 13, 600 litres of water a minute through a 90 mm nozzle at a pressure of 7 bar. Elevation and lateral direction of the fire stream is usually controlled through an arrangement of gears, the monitor being mounted in many cases on the forecastle. As these monitors form an important part of the equipment of a fireboat, they are dealt with and illustrated in the *Manual, Part 7: Chapter 1, 'Fireboats and their Equipment'*

### (2) Turntable ladders

All turntable ladders are equipped to act as water towers and for this purpose carry a special monitor which is mounted at the head of the ladder. Details of the construction and use of this type of monitor are to be found in the *Manual, Book 5 Chapter 4, Turntable Ladders'*.

### (3) Hydraulic platforms

Monitors are also to be found fitted on the platform of hydraulic platforms. They generally have a greater degree of manoeuvrability than those on turntable ladders.

## 3 Radial branches

The radial branch was designed to facilitate the handling of very large jets, but is not widely used by brigades now. The one illustrated in Fig. 6.4 is designed for use with nozzles up to 50 mm in diameter. The branch holder consists of two double stays, one (a) pointed at the bottom end to give a purchase on the ground to the front, and the other (b) fitted with a steel-studded plate (c) which also rests on the ground to the rear. The double rear stay carries at the upper end a branch (d) fitted with a 90 mm 'Surelock' coupling (e) for connection to 90 mm hose (f). This stay, which is hinged on the base plate, slides up and down on the double front stay which acts as a guide. The movement is controlled by a simple winch gear (g) carried at the head of the front stay which controls the elevation of the jet. A locking screw (h) on the sliding carriage is provided to clamp the branch in postion and thus take the weight off the cable (i) and winch gear. Above the winch gear is a handle (j) used by the branchman to control the lateral movement of the branch.

When working under high pressure with a large nozzle (k) the radial branch requires considerable quantities of water and twin lines of hose are necessary to supply it (see Plate 11). The branch is normally fed by a 5·2 m length of 90 mm hose, usually rubber-

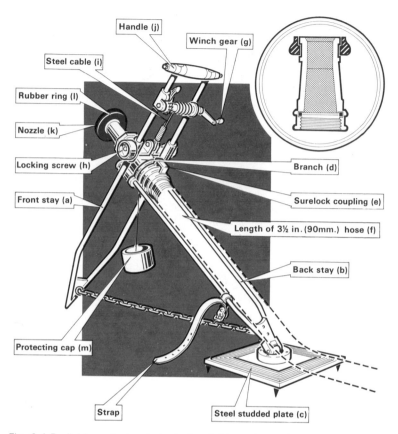

Fig. 6.4 Radial branch. Inset: typical radial branch nozzle.

lined, fitted with 'Surelock' couplings. The hose rests on the rear stay of the branch, and is connected to the 90 mm outlet of a special dividing breeching (described in Chapter 8), which is fed by two lines of delivery hose. The nozzles used (Fig. 6.4, *inset*) range from 38 mm to 50 mm diameter and are usually fitted with a rubber ring (l) to protect them from damage. A nozzle protection cap (m) is also provided for use when the branch is stowed away.

Owing to the difficulty in obtaining spare parts, radial branches are generally only kept as non-mobile special equipment by those brigades that still have them, and are gradually being replaced by ground monitors.

# Chapter 7
# Standpipes, collecting heads and suction hose fittings

## 1 Standpipes

Because it would be impracticable to couple hose directly to a hydrant, a piece of equipment known as a standpipe is used to extend the outlet of the hydrant above ground level. Use of a standpipe overcomes access difficulties caused by the restricted size of hydrant pits and the depth below ground at which hydrant outlets are normally located. It also enables kinking to be avoided when connecting hose to hydrant supplies. In certain obsolete types of hydrant, such as the ball hydrant, the standpipe provided the only means of controlling the flow.

The term standpipe normally denotes the complete fitting, including the head, although with some types, the shaft and head are separate fittings which can be disconnected. In the past, standpipes were usually made of polished solid drawn copper tubes with gunmetal mountings, but now they are normally constructed in alloys of copper or aluminium in accordance with B.S. 336.

## 2 Standpipe bases

The type of connection required at the base of a standpipe is determined by the type of hydrant outlet used. The *Manual* Book 7, Chapters 7 and 8 deals with the subject of water mains and hydrants and describes various types which have been used in this country during the past century. It goes on to describe the patterns of standard hydrant now in common use throughout the country and refers to BS. 750, which lays down the specifications to which all new hydrants are manufactured.

### a. Standard bases

In the past there were at one time over 50 different types of hydrant outlet in existence and this of course meant a similar number of different standpipe bases—a factor which complicated mutual assistance arrangements between different authorities.Since 1948, however, considerable progress has been made in the conversion of hydrant outlets to the standard 65 mm round-thread type, and standpipes with bases to fit the standard hydrant outlet are now in common use.

Specifications for the standard round-thread standpipe base (Fig. 7.1) for connection to standard hydrant outlets are contained in B.S. 336. The base casting, now normally made of alloys of either copper or aluminium, has an external diameter of about 100 mm and is threaded from the bottom with 25 mm of female round thread which terminates in a recess designed to take a leather washer. The internal diameter of the bore of the standpipe is not specified in the British Standard as this is left to the discretion of manufacturers, but is usually about 58 mm.

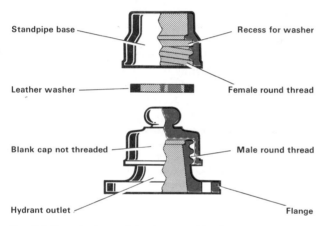

Fig. 7.1 Standard standpipe base and hydrant outlet.

### b. Other types of base

Obsolete types of hydrant may still be found to exist in some places and in addition to the standard base, other types which may be encountered include:

(1) 'V' thread base

The 'V' thread base is similar in principle to the standard round-thread type, but it has a finer thread designed to fit 'V' thread hydrant outlets.

(2) Instaneous bases

One type has a male standpipe base to fit a female instantaneous hydrant outlet. Another type has a female base to fit a male instantaneous hydrant outlet. In the latter case the standpipe has two levers passing up either side of the shaft, pivoting about 200 mm from the base, and these are necessary to enable the lugs to be disengaged from the male hydrant outlet in the close confines of a hydrant pit. By pressing these levers inwards the female lugs are withdrawn, allowing the standpipe to be removed.

### (3) Lugged type base

With this type the connection takes the form of a female coupling on the hydrant outlet having two right-angled lugs diametrically opposed to each other, while the male coupling on the standpipe base has two square-shaped lugs on a threaded collar which engage the right-angled lugs of the female coupling.

### (4) Bayonet type base

In the bayonet type of connection the standpipe base has a female coupling which is slotted to engage small wedge-shaped lugs on the male coupling of the hydrant outlet.

Most of the standpipes fitted with a bayonet or lug connection have a short pair of ·handles at the top for asssisting in making the connection to the hydrant.

## 3 Shafts and heads

### a. Shafts

At one time standpipe shafts used in different districts varied considerably in length owing to the differences in the depth of hydrant pits, and crews working outside their areas sometimes found that the shafts carried on their appliances were not long enough to enable them to make connection.To overcome this dificulty, a fitting known as a standpipe extension piece was used consisting simply of a short standpipe shaft about 300 mm and inserted as necessary between the hydrant outlet and the standpipe proper. However, with the progress which has been made since World War II in the hydrant conversion programme, this problem is not so prevalent nowadays because the general aim is for the hydrant outlet to be not more than about 300 mm below the surface of the hydrant pit cover.

Although there are many different patterns of standpipe in use throughout the country, they are now normally made in accordance with BS. 336. The overall length of standpipe shafts will be found to vary with the requirements of different users, but most standpipes in current use are about 1 m in length and those illustrated in Fig. 7.2 can be taken as representative of the types in most common use.

### b. Standpipe heads

Standpipe heads vary greatly and may be made with either single or double outlets.Fig. 7.2(1), shows a head with a single outlet

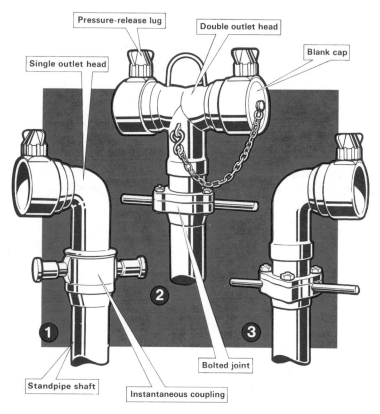

Fig. 7.2 Standpipe heads.

terminating in a standard instantaneous female coupling with a single pressure-release lug. It connects to the standpipe shaft by means of a standard instantaneous coupling which allows the head to swivel.Fig. 7.2(2), illustrates an example of a typical standpipe head with two outlets, the connection to the shaft in this case being in the form of a bolted joint. A gland is incorporated to permit the head to rotate as necessary, and a blank cap is provided on the end of a short length of chain in case only one outlet is required to be used. Fig. 7.2(3), illustrates a similar type of standpipe head, but with one outlet only.

## 4 Collecting heads

A collecting head consists of a metal casting, usually made of aluminium alloy having on one side a number of inlets (two, three or four), according to the capacity of the pump, fitted with standard male instantaneous delivery hose couplings. On the other side is a single outlet with a standard female screw-type suction hose coupling for connection to the pump inlet.

Each inlet on a collecting head is fitted with a non-return valve. Some manufacturers use mushroom-type valves while others use clack-type valves which are claimed to be hydraulically more efficient.The mushroom-type non-return valve used in collecting heads (Fig. 7.3) has either a synthetic rubber or a ground metal

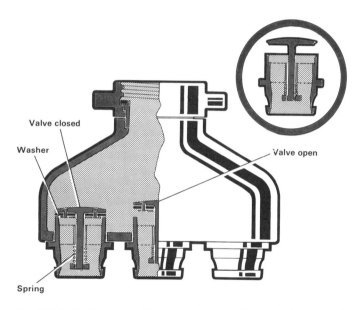

Fig. 7.3 Collecting head (three-way): inset: alternative type of valve seat.

face which is held against a seating by means of a spiral spring. The action of water entering the inlet under pressure forces the valve off its seating and allows the water to pass on through the collecting box.

Fig. 7.4 illustrates a clack-type non-return valve which is used in some collecting heads. This type of valve is hinged at the top

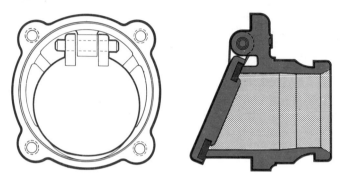

Fig. 7.4 Clack-type non-return valve.

and recessed around the periphery to take a synthetic rubber washer which makes a watertight joint against its seating when the valve is under pressure. The clack-type valves will not operate if the collecting head is used upside down; therefore this type of collecting head is usually marked to enable the top side to be easily identified.

When using collecting heads the pressure on the inlet side should be kept as low as possible and the aim should be to maintain, without any appreciable build-up of pressure, a steady supply which equals that which is demanded from the output side.

## 5 Suction strainers

There are two types of suction strainer used by fire brigades, and they are known respectively as (a) metal strainers, and (b) basket strainers. The design of both types of strainer is covered by B.S. 336.

### a. Metal strainers

These are designed and used to prevent solid objects which might damage the pump, from being drawn up through the suction hose when working from open water. A typical metal suction strainer which is in common use is illustrated inFig. 7.5(1). It consists of a copper or alloy strainer, cylindrical in shape and perforated with holes sufficient in size and number not to restrict the maximum capacity of the suction hose, yet small enough to prevent entry of pieces of wood, stones or other solid objects.

Metal strainers are fitted with a female suction hose coupling and made in sizes to fit the standard sizes of suction hose.

Sometimes it is necessary to pump from shallow water of only a few inches deep, and to facilitate this, specially designed low-level metal strainers of various patterns are produced. Fig. 7.5(2), illustrates one example of a low-level strainer which is produced in sizes to fit standard sizes of suction hose. Water can only enter via the bottom of the strainer which stands on four squat legs and a pump can continue to lift water so long as the bottom of the strainer remains submerged.

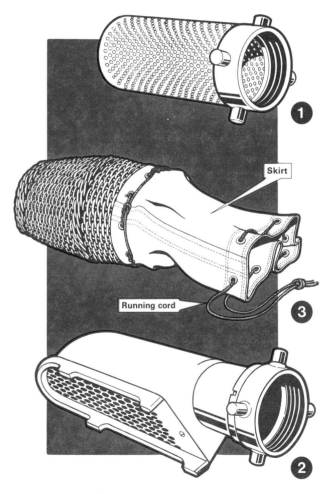

Fig. 7.5 Strainers: (1) typical metal strainer; (2) a low-level strainer; (3) the basket strainer used in conjunction with the metal strainer.

### b. The basket strainer

The basket strainer (Fig. 7.5(3)) is used in conjunction with the metal strainer, but never alone. When resting on a soft surface such as mud, the copper strainer tends to sink in, thus reducing the percentage of its surface area which remains effective. The basket strainer, acting as an outer shell, rests in the mud, and having a larger surface area, still leaves a considerable proportion exposed, so allowing the copper strainer to function unimpaired. The basket strainer also tends to protect the copper strainer from damage. It also assists in removing particles from the water entering the suction; these, though small enough to pass through the perforations in the metal strainer, would tend to damage the pump mechanism

Basket strainers are cylindrical in shape and are constructed of woven wickerwork with one open end to which is attached a piece of canvas, known as the skirt. This has a running a cord which secures the basket around the suction, thus preventing the water from entering the mouth of the strainer without passing between the basketwork.

## 6 Suction crutches and saddles

The primary object of using suction crutches and saddles is to prevent abrasion and kinking of suction hose when it has to be laid over rought surfaces and sharp edges. They are usually made up locally to various simple designs. Suction saddles, usually of wood, are constructed so that the underside conveniently fits over the top of obstacles such as low walls whilst the upper side is shaped to recieve the suction hose.

# Chapter 8
# Breechings, adaptors, miscellaneous hose fittings and ramps

## 1 Breechings

Breechings are generally used for two purposes: (a) for uniting two lines of hose into one, when they are known as collecting breechings, or (b) for dividing one line of hose into two, known in this case as dividing breechings.

### a. Collecting breechings

Collecting breechings normally have two inlets and one outlet and there are two basic types:

    (1) the type where the two inlets and the single outlet are all designed to take hose couplings of the same diameter, and

    (2) the type where the two inlets are designed to take hose couplings of one diameter while the outlet is designed to take a coupling of different diameter.

The design of collecting breechings with standard instantaneous couplings is covered by B.S. 336, and an example of this type of breeching is illustrated in Fig. 8.1(1). It has instantaneous male

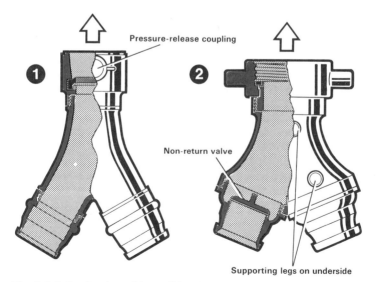

Fig. 8.1 Collecting breechings: (1) with standard instantaneous couplings; (2) breeching for use with a monitor.

couplings on both inlet legs and an instantaneous female single-lug pressure-release coupling of the same diameter on the single outlet.

Fig. 8.1(2), illustrates one type of collecting breeching sometimes used in conjunction with a short length of 90 mm diameter hose for feeding radial branches or monitors. It may have a 'Surelock' or an instantaneous female outlet instead of the round-threaded connection shown in the diagram. The supporting legs on the underside are fitted to ensure that the breeching is placed on the ground in the correct position, because if it is placed upside down, the flap-type non-return valves would not operate. Some collecting breechings are fitted with mushroom-type non-return valves. A collecting breeching with control facilities is shown in Fig. 6.3(1).

## b. Dividing breechings

Dividing breechings have one inlet and two outlets, and the type illustrated in Fig. 8.2(1) is included in B.S. 336. It has a male instantaneous coupling on the single inlet and female instantaneous couplings on the two outlets.

As has been said, the primary purpose of dividing breechings it to divide one hose-line into two, and this practice is adopted, when pressure is adequate, to providde two jets instead of one, e.g. for such purposes as cooling down. In such circumstances it is not uncommon for a 70 mm hose-line to be divided into two lines of 45 mm hose—a good example of one advantage of the use of a standard sized coupling on all sizes of delivery hose. A disadvantage of this practice is that water cannot be shut off from one line of hose without also shutting it off from the other line.

The type of breeching illustrated in Fig. 8.2(2) has facilities for controlling, by means of a valve, the flow to either or both outlets, and this is commonly known as a 'control dividing breeching'. There are various patterns of this type of control breeching, but although the constructional detail may differ, the operating positions for the valve are usually marked clearly on the body of the breeching. One advantage of the control type breeching is that either hose-line can be shut down without closing the other, a practice which is convenient when adding or removing lengths of hose from the working lines. They are also of particular value on heath and similar fires when long hose-lines are in use and when water is scarce.

## 2 Adaptors

Adaptors are fittings made for the purpose of connecting hose or suction couplings of different types or sizes or for connecting the

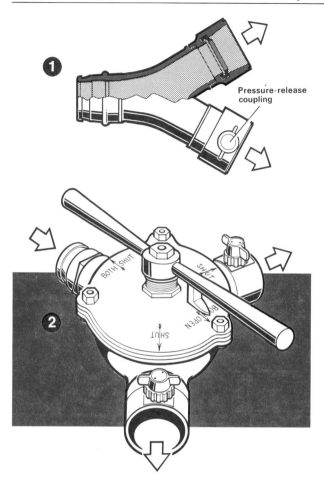

Fig. 8.2 Dividing breechings: (1) with instantaneous couplings; (2) a control breeching.

male to male or female to female parts of the same type of coupling. They consist of a metal fitting terminating at each end in a coupling and average between 100 and 150 mm in length.Adaptors are usually cast as one fitting, except in the case of screwed female ends where the nut and sleeve are separate.

## a. Delivery hose adaptors

Adaptors for use with delivery hose couplings fall into two broad categories:

(1) Adaptors for connecting male or female parts of the same type of coupling:

| | |
|---|---|
| male to male, female to female | round-thread, 'V' thread or instantaneous. |

(2) Adaptors for connecting two different types of coupling:

| | |
|---|---|
| male to male, female to female | round-thread to instantaneous (Fig. 8.3); round-thread to Surelock'; 'V' thread to instantaneous; instantaneous to hermaphrodite. |
| male to female | round-thread to 'V' thread. |

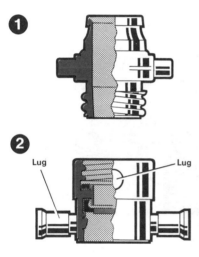

Fig. 8.3 Adaptors: (1) round-thread male to instantaneous male; (2) round-thread female to instantaneous female.

Special adaptors for connection into the delivery and into the suction line of a pump are also used with a multiple jet inductor for the larger size foam-making branches.

### b. Hydrant adaptors

With the progress that has been made during recent years in the standardisation of hydrant outlets throughout the country, there is no need in many brigades for hydrant adaptors. They may, however, still be found in areas where all hydrants have not yet been standardised. Prior to the inception of the hydrant conversion scheme, numerous types of hydrant adaptor were used by fire brigades to enable standpipes of different patterns to be connected to the various hydrant outlets, and they catered for such combinations as 'V' to round-thread; female bayonet to female instantaneous; female round-thread to lugged, and lugged to male 'V' thread.

### c. Hose-reel adaptors

Hose-reel adaptors are used to enable hose-reel couplings to be connected to hose-reel equipment and to other types of coupling. Fig. 8.4(1) illustrates an adaptor which enables a hose-reel coupling with a BSP thread to be connected to a standard instantaneous

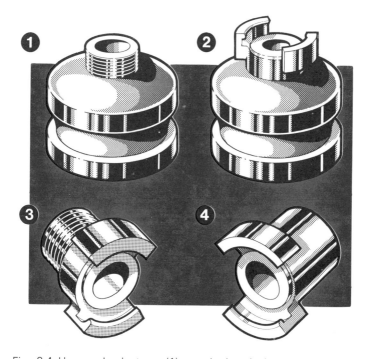

Fig. 8.4 Hose-reel adaptors: (1) standard male instantaneous to male hose-reel BSP thread; (2) standard male instantaneous to hermaphrodite hose-reel coupling; (3) male BSP to hermaphrodite; (4) female BSP to hermaphrodite.

female coupling and is often used to enable a length of hose-reel hose to be connected to a standpipe outlet, or to a length of delivery hose. Another adaptor used for the same purpose (Fig. 8.4(2)) enables a hermaphrodite hose-reel coupling to be connected to a standard instantaneous female outlet.

Fig. 8.4(3 and 4) show adaptors which enable hermaphrodite hose-reel couplings to be connected to male and female British Standard pipe thread connections. The female threaded one (4) is commonly used to connect a hose-reel coupling to the male threaded outlet of the hose-reel.

### d. Suction hose adaptors

Although they are not often used nowadays by fire brigades, various types of suction adaptor exist for such purposes as connecting delivery hose to hard suction or to a pump inlet, or for interconnecting two lengths of suction which are of different diameters. The examples of suction adaptors illustrated in Fig. 8.5 show (1) male suction to female instantaneous delivery; (2) female suction to male instantaneous delivery; (3) male suction to male round-thread delivery and (4) female suction to female round-thread delivery. Adaptors for connecting suction hose of different diameters usually have a female coupling at one end and a male at the other.

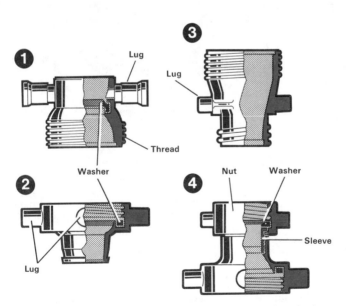

Fig. 8.5 Suction adaptors: (1) male suction to female instantaneous delivery; (2) female suction to male instantaneous delivery; (3) male suction to male round-thread delivery; (4) female suction to female round-thread delivery.

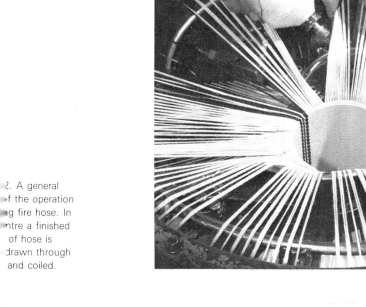

1. Hose weaving
circular loom. A
of weft yarn is
inserted
en warps prior
loom being
ted.

2. A general
f the operation
g fire hose. In
ntre a finished
of hose is
drawn through
and coiled.

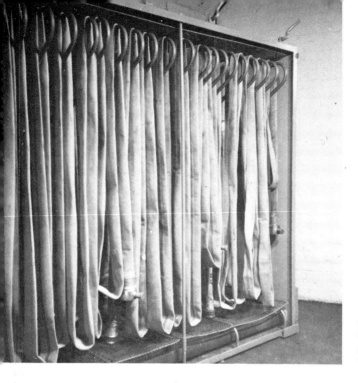

Plate 3. A hose-drying cabinet, with electric heaters at the bottom and ventilating trunking at the top.

Plate 4. A typical brick built drill tower incorporating hose-drying facilities at the rear.

e 5. The extractor fan at the top of the hose-drying tower shown in Plate 6.

e 6. Upward view of the inside of a hose-drying tower, showing hose
)ended for drying.

Plate 7. A hose coupling binder which works on the principle described on page 46.

Plate 8. Another type of hose coupling binder.

Plate 9. A diffuser branch in use, adjusted to give a fire system.

Plate 10. The same diffuser branch producing a wide spray.

Plate 11. A radial branch in use at a large fire.

Plate 12. A rope walk at a cordage manufacturers. The length of working space required is considerable.

13. Method of testing a lowering line. The strain should be progressively
d until the line is being subjected to the combined weight of all six men.

14. A railing expander in use to release a boy's head which has become
ed in some railings.

Plate 15. Electric floodlights and cable reels, which are operated from the generator on an emergency tender.

Plate 16. A propane/butane portable floodlight.

## 3 Miscellaneous hose fittings

### a. Gooseneck

The gooseneck (Fig. 8.6) consists of a short length of pipe of uniform bore throughout, curved in a semi-circle and fitted with a coupling at one end for attachment to a line of hose in place of

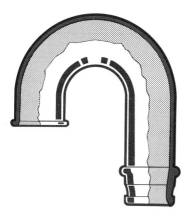

Fig. 8.6 Gooseneck.

a branch. This item of equipment was originally designed during World War II and was used for filling emergency water supply tanks. It is simply hooked over the edge of the tank or dam and forms a convenient open-ended connection for the end of a line of hose. It obviates kinking of hose over a tank edge and will stay securely in position without the need for lashing.

### b. Elbow-for-nozzle

This is a metal attachment (Fig. 8.7(1)), which can be fitted between the branch and the nozzle so as to enable a jet of water to be delivered at right angles to the branch. This extension to the branch is sometimes used for attacking fires in a basement or ship's hold when, for various reasons, it is not practicable to use a normal straight branch.

## c. Blank cap

A blank cap is used for blanking off an outlet or an inlet, such as a pump outlet or suction inlet. It consists of a metal casting blanked off at one end with a male or female coupling connection at the other. Fig. 8.7(2) illustrates a blank cap with a male instantaneous connection for use on a female instantaneous coupling (e.g. as on a pump outlet). A blank cap for use on a suction inlet has a round-thread connection of the appropriate size.

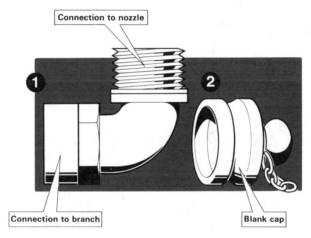

Fig. 8.7 (1) Elbow-for-nozzle; (2) Blank cap.

## d. Release valve

After a turntable ladder monitor has been in use, back pressure of the water trapped in the hose leading to the monitor can make it difficult to break hose couplings at ground level, and a device known as a release valve is sometimes used to enable this water to be released. The valve may be mounted as a fixture at the rear of the appliance.

The release valve used for this purpose consists of a metal casting with standard instantaneous couplings at each end which can be inserted in the hose-line at the foot of the ladder. Operation of a simple hand-controlled rotary valve quickly releases water from the monitor hose-line through a waste outlet provided in the casting.

## 4 Cleaning and maintenance of hose fittings

All hose fittings and equipment should be regularly examined and cleaned to ensure that they are always in good condition and ready for immediate operational use. A systematic routine for this work not only ensures that equipment is maintained in first-class condition at all times, but also that personnel become thoroughly familiar with it and get to know exactly where each item is kept on the various types of appliance. This knowledge is essential if crews are to operate quickly and efficiently, particularly when working in the dark.

When cleaning hose fittings, particular attention should be given to ensuring that all moving parts operate freely, that washers are in good condition, that any rough edges or projections which might damage the hose are smoothed or removed, and that residue from paint or polish is removed from places where it may tend to block holes, threads or passages and thus reduce operating efficiency. Couplings which, due to damage, cannot be connected without difficulty should be taken out of service until such time as they can be repaired or replaced. A faulty coupling left in service may well be the cause of delay in getting a vitally important line of hose to work on a fire.

Nozzles depend for their efficiency upon the true circular shape of the orifice and upon an undamaged lip, so care should be taken when cleaning them. Cleaning by pulling a rag back and forth through the nozzle is bad practice, as this in time wears the bore to an irregular shape and at the same time tends to destroy the knife-edge of the orifice lip. When dealing with light alloy hose fittings, all threads and moving parts should be treated with special molybdenised grease or oil which serves both as a lubricant and as a preventative against corrosion.

## 5 Hose ramps

One of the problems which often have to be faced when dealing with large fires is the obstruction of roads by lines of charged hose. Attempts to force heavy vehicles over it may well cause damage to the hose; therefore special equipment in the form of hose ramps is carried on most fire appliances and used to enable wheeled vehicles to cross charged hose-lines without dragging or damaging the hose.

Hose ramps of various patterns are used, but they are all designed to provide a sloping path up and over the hose with sufficient clearance to prevent contact between vehicle wheels or tyres and the charged hose. Most hose ramps are designed to accommodate standard 70 mm delivery hose, but some types can also be used for ramping 90 mm diameter hose.

## a. Wooden ramps

Fig. 8.8 illustrates several types of wooden hose ramp which consist of wedge-shaped pieces of wood joined by either straps, ropes or strips of condemned hose so as to provide channels of about 90 mm wide into which charged hose can be laid. The ramp makes an incline on each side to carry the wheels of vehicular traffic safely over the hose. Fig. 8.8(2) shows a ramp fitted on each side with an apron of old hose or belting. An apron of this sort greatly improves the efficiency of ramps because it obviates their tendency to drag or be pushed along by vehicle wheels. The weight of the vehicle is first transferred to the apron and thus holds the ramp firmly in position as the wheels mount the incline.

When more than one line of hose requires ramping and only single-line ramps are available, they should be arranged as shown in Fig. 8.8(3). This obviates the series of troughs formed if ramps are laid as in Fig. 8.8(4), when they are liable to be easily displaced by the movement of traffic.

Some ramps have a rectangular section which is connected between the two wedges to provide channels in which two or more lines of hose can be laid (Fig. 8.8(1)). A modification of this type of ramp which can be expanded to take additional lines of hose by means of extra sections linked by interlocking metal rods is illustrated in Fig. 8.9(1).

## b. Metal ramps

Ramps of various types made of steel are used by some fire brigades, one example of which is illustrated in Fig. 8.9(2 and 3). This type of ramp consists of interlocking sections, the angle of the slope of the end units varying between 8 and 12 degrees, and sections are added as necessary to accommodate the required number of hose-lines. When laying these ramps over a number of lines of hose so as to form a solid crossover, it is advantageous to stagger the central sections by half a length (Fig. 8.9(3)) as this breaks the joints and thus reduces movement when traffic is passing over them.

With ramps which are only between 600 to 900 mm wide, it is of course necessary to lay down, for each length of hose, two ramps at a sufficient distance apart to take the nearside and offside wheels of vehicles. Where there is a great variation in the width of vehicles passing over, a pair of ramps for each track may be necessary.

During recent years, metal ramps made of light alloys have become popular with many brigades and one example of this type of ramp is illustrated in Fig. 8.10. This particular ramp is light in weight and made of standard alloy materials, and it gives the

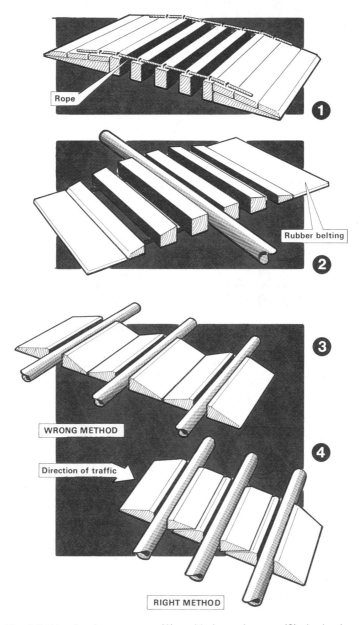

Fig. 8.8 Wooden hose ramps: (1) multi-channel ramp; (2) single-channel ramp with aprons; (3 and 4) right and wrong ways of ramping several lines of hose with single-channel ramps.

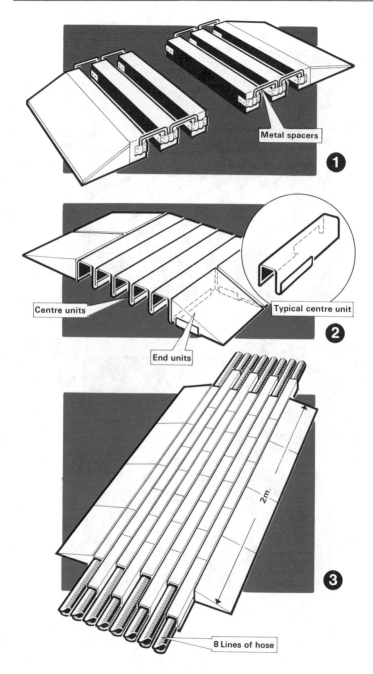

Fig. 8.9 Metal hose ramps: (1) multi-channel type linked by metal rods; (2) steel channel section ramps; (3) staggered arrangement of steel channel section ramps.

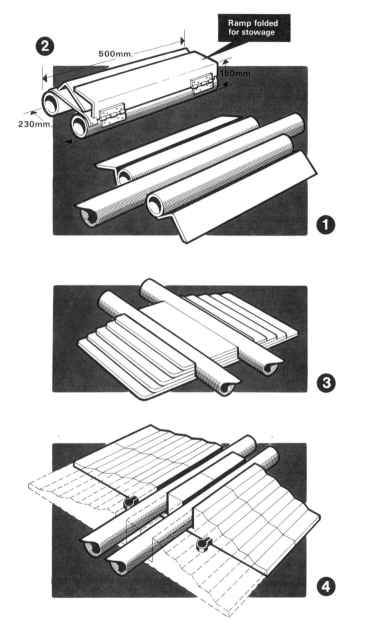

Fig. 8.10 (1) a light alloy ramp shown in use; (2) the ramp folded for stowage; (3) a typical reinforced rubber ramp; (4) reinforced-rubber ramp made with interlocking units.

minimum impedance to vehicular traffic because the diameter of the tubing used is only slightly greater than that of the charged hose. Hinged approach slopes enable the ramp to be folded for convenient stowage to a size of $500 \times 230 \times 150$ mm.

### c. Rubber ramps

Ramps made of reinforced rubber are now in widespread use by fire brigades. A typical ramp of this type is shown in Fig. 8.10(3), whilst the ramp shown in Fig. 8.10(4) can be interlocked with adjacent units so that a ramp of any required width can be laid down.

# Part 3
# Ropes and lines

Rope-making is one of the oldest industries practised by man and its origin is lost in antiquity. It is, however, known that the ancient Egyptians possessed the art with a high degree of skill, for when the doors of the inner chamber of the tomb of Tutankhamun were opened, it was found that they had been secured by a length of 100 mm rope. The quality and workmanship shown were of a high order, so the industry goes back well over three thousand years.

Wire rope is frequently regarded as of comparatively recent origin, but a piece of bronze rope now in a museum at Naples indicates that wire ropes were used by the Romans over two thousand years ago. Modern wire ropes differ from those of ancient times only in that they are made of different materials, by machine, and in a greater variety of constructions.

Terms, such as *hawser*, *cable*, *rope*, *lines*, etc. used in rope-making are often used indiscriminately by laymen. These terms have precise meanings, and a glossary of the more general terms in use will be found at the end of this Part, but it should be noted that ropes cut to specific lengths for particular purposes are known in the fire service as *lines*, whilst wire ropes used for extending escapes and turntable ladders are known as *cables*.

Lines form an important item in the equipment carried on fire brigade appliances, and their manufacture, the various types in use and the necessity for proper care and maintenance of natural fibre lines are dealt with in the first three chapters of this Part. In order to use a line to maximum advantage, it is essential that every fireman should be completely competent in the tying of each of the standard knots, bends and hitches. He should be able to make each one so automatically that it can be made, as is often necessary, in complete darkness, under difficult conditions of smoke and urgency. Finally in the Part is a chapter on general rope work.

# Chapter 9
# Construction of rope

Rope may be of either fibre of metal or sometimes of mixed construction, though in the latter case it is the metal part which carries the load. The general description applied to all forms of fibre rope, line and twine is *cordage*, and ropes made of metal are referred to as *wire ropes*.

## 1 Natural fibre rope

Rope, as generally used in the fire service, is made principally of:

(a) *Italian hemp*, a bast fibre obtained from the stalks of the hemp plant. The fibre is soft, pliable and considerably stronger than other hemps;

(b) *manila*, a fibre obtained from the leaf sheaths of the abaca plant;

and to a much less extent of:

(c) *sisal*, a fibre obtained from the leaves of the sisal plant;

(d) *coir*, a fibre obtained from the husk of the coconut;

(e) *cotton*, a fibre obtained from the seed pods of the cotton plant.

Italian hemp is acknowledged as the best fibre for fire brigade work, particularly for lines used for rescue purposes, as it is less likely to swell when wetted and, owing to the softness of the fibres, is more flexible. It can, therefore, be used over shorter radius curves and so has a longer life. The availability of Italian hemp, however, is decreasing and where manufacturers are able to supply it, the cost is relatively high. This is due not only to the short supply of top quality Italian hemp, but also to the increasing use of man-made fibre for the construction of all types of rope. A request for an Italian hemp line may have to be met on a 'one-off' basis even if the hemp is available.

Manila, on the other hand, makes an excellant general purpose rope and is less expensive. Sisal, although about as strong as Grade 2 manila, is not normally used since it swells considerably when it is wet and is liable to be slippery. Coir, owing to its lightness, will float on water, and so is used on fireboats for getting lines of hose and warps (i.e. lines used for mooring vessels) ashore. It has not the strength of the preceding types and should on no account be used where any lifting is involved. Cotton rope has a high resilience and is soft to handle, but is particularly susceptible to damage from chafing.

All the above materials are natural fibres and may be given rot-proofing treatment. They have, however, only slight elasticity and for shock-absorbing properties reliance must be placed on the structure of the rope. With the increasing production of man-made fibres which are inherently rot-proof and are capable of withstanding shock loads many times greater than natural fibres, lines manufactured from man-made fibres are being used increasingly in the fire service.

## 2. Man-made fibre rope

The two principal fibres used for cordage are:

(a) *nylon*, a man-made fibre with a complex form structure of carbon, nitrogen, oxygen and hydrogen, and

(b) a polyester fibre derived by chemical synthesis from the products of mineral oil cracking; polyester fibre in the United Kingdom is marketed under the trade name of *terylene.*

Both are extruded and drawn into very fine filaments of a silvery-white sheen and soft silky testure. The filaments are continuous, so that in cordage the advantages of continuity of filaments combined with accurately controlled manufacturing conditions result in uniformity of strength throughout the whole length of ropes made from these materials. This is not so in rope made from natural fibres, which is subject to variations in fibre structure and strength.

The finished rope is smooth, flexible and pleasant to handle. It runs well over blocks or pulleys and can be knotted, seized or spliced in the normal manner. In splicing, however, additional tucks are recommended (see page 161), as the highly elastic nature of the materials can lead to undoing of a normal splice under rapid loading conditions. Four full tucks are recommended in BS 3367—'Fire Brigade Rescue Lines'; this standard also gives details of a special splice for the plaited polyester fibre lines (see also page 161).

Tensile strength is an important property of all rope, and both nylon and terylene are outstanding in this respect, being approximately twice as strong, size for size, as rope made from the highest-grade vegetable fibre. Other valuable properties of man-made fibres are:

(i)   ability to absorb shock loads;

(ii)  ability to withstand repeated loadings of a high order without failure;

(iii) little swelling on immersion in water;

(iv) they can be stored wet without degradation by rot or mildew.

Terylene rope is slightly less extensible at low loads and is highly resistant to most acids. Nylon rope has a slightly higher breaking strength than terylene, size for size, and can absorb more energy; it is also highly resistant to most alkalis. The comparatively low stretch of terylene makes it suitable for use as a rescue line.

## 3 Wire rope

Wire rope is a combination of steel wires arranged around a central fibre core. Steel reaches the wire mills in the form of rods, which are first cleaned in acid to remove rust. After heat treatment to ensure uniformity in tensile strength, ductility, etc. they are cleaned again before being drawn cold through a series of dies each of which gets successively smaller until the required size is reached. After drawing, the wire may be galvanised according to requirements.

The breaking load of wire rope is considerably greater than that of fibre rope of equivalent size, but it is far less flexible and more difficult to handle. Its use by fire brigades is, therefore, generally limited to equipment which is operated by means of a winch, such as wheeled escapes, turntable ladders and some extension ladders.

## 4 Methods of manufacture

### a. Natural fibre rope

The fibre is received at the rope works packed in bales and requires considerable combing and cleaning before it is ready for ropemaking. The first process is the *preparation* of the fibre, consisting of a series of combings with the object of arranging the fibres in a parallel order. After combing the fibre is known as a *sliver*.

In the next process the silver is spun into a yarn, during which operation a permanent twist is mechanically inserted, and the resultant yarn is wound on to bobbins. Subsequent processing depends on the construction required; the yarn is twisted into strands which are laid together to produce a three- or four-strand rope. In addition to laying, the strands may be plaited to produce a plaited rope.

### b. Man-made fibre rope

No preparation of the fibres is necessary as the yarn is received in a continuous filament, ready wound on bobbins. Only three main processes are involved: twisting the yarns together, forming the strands and laying. These operations are carried out on normal rope-making machinery as used for natural fibre rope.

### c. Wire rope

Wire from the mills is received at the rope works in coils, and three main stages are involved in making wire into rope. First, the wire is wound on to the bobbins for loading on to stranding machines, where the requisite number of wires are twisted together to form strands. In forming a strand, one of the wires is used as a centre core and the others are twisted round it, although a fibre core may sometimes be used. Finally, the strands are *closed*, that is, the required number of strands, according to the type of rope, are twisted or laid round a central core, usually of hemp.

This central fibre core in a wire rope is of equal importance with the wires in the strands. In addition to preventing undue friction of the wires in adjacent strands, it provides an elastic base to allow relative displacement of the wire strands when the rope is flexed round a sheave. The presence of moisture in the fibre core of a wire rope is obviously undesirable, and during the manufacturing process, the fibre core is rendered as moisture-free as possible before being impregnated with a suitable lubricant.

## 5 Laying

### a. Natural and man-made fibre rope

When wound on to bobbins the yarns are ready to be made up into strands, which consist of a series of yarns twisted together and which are made up in one of two ways, i.e. either in a 'rope walk' or by a special form of machine. The former is still largely employed for making fibre rope and in its essentials differs little from the method used for centuries. The rope walk (see plate 12), consists of a long narrow shed which may be as much as 300 m or more in length, since rope cannot be made by this method in one piece of a greater length than that of the rope walk. Rope is normally made in lengths not exceeding 220 m. The appropriate number of yarns are drawn off the bobbins and twisted together on the rope walk to form a strand. Three or four strands are thus formed and these are then twisted together to form the rope. This operation is known as *laying*. When laid up, the finished rope is readly for coiling.

In order to prevent a rope from unravelling, the yarns making up the individual strands are twisted together in the opposite direction to that in which the strands are twisted when made up into rope. Rope may be twisted or *laid up* either right hand or left hand, and is then known as having a *right-hand* or a *left-hand lay*, respectively. This direction of twist or lay in cordage is now referred to by the symbols 'S' and 'Z' (Fig. 9.1), the direction

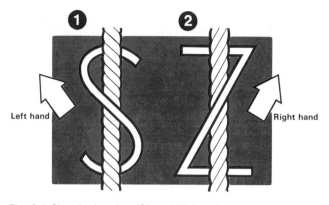

Fig. 9.1 Sketch showing 'S' and 'Z' lays in rope.

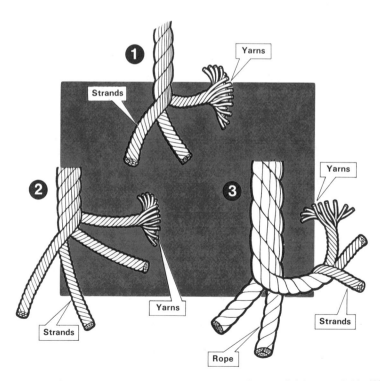

Fig. 9.2 Sketches showing the construction of rope; (1) hawser-laid; (2) shroud-laid; (3) 9-strand cable-laid.

following the line of the central portion of the letter. The lay can be determined by looking at the rope; if the strands run away from the body from left to right, it is 'Z' or right-hand lay (Fig. 9.1(2)); if from right to left, it is 'S' or left-hand lay (Fig. 9.1(1)).

The angle of the lay is important and is defined in rope specifications, being not less than 37 degrees for plain or hawser-laid and 39 degrees for shroud-laid rope. A few degrees either way in the angle of the strand has a considerable effect on the breaking load of a finished rope.

Fibre rope is usually made up in one of the following constructions:

(1) 3-*strand* (plain or hawser-laid), Z-lay, in which the three strands are laid together (Fig 9.2(1)).

(2) 4-*strand* (shroud-laid), Z-lay, consisting of four strands laid together (Fig. 9.2(2)).

(3) 9-*strand* (cable-laid), S-lay, consisting of three hawser, Z-lay ropes (Fig. 9.2(3)).

The size of a rope is expressed in terms of its circumference. The size is actually determined by the size of the yarns, i.e. the number of threads in the yarn, and the number of yarns in a strand. For example, BS 2052—'Ropes made from coir, hemp, manila and sisal--—states that a 25 mm 3-strand hawser-laid manila rope has 24 threads to each yarn and a minimum of three yarns to each strand, whereas a 50 mm rope of the same type has a minimum of eleven yarns to each strand.

### b. Wire rope

Wire rope is made up in either *ordinary lay* or *Lang's lay*. For ordinary lay, the wires in the strand are twisted in one direction and the strands are laid in the opposite. Lang's lay differs from ordinary lay in that the strands are laid to form the rope in the same direction as the wires are twisted in the strands. The use of rope made up in Lang's lay is, however, limited generally to cases where both ends of the rope are made fast and the load secured against rotation. For general use, wire rope is made up in ordinary lay and laid right-hand, which is the standard direction. Left-hand lay rope is made, but is not in common use.

Wire rope is made in a number of various constructions, many of which are for special purposes, but only a few are necessary to cover all general applications. The types generally used in engineering have six strands, each strand containing 19, 24 or 37 wires (Fig. 9.3). When describing the construction of wire rope, the number of strands is quoted first and then the number of wires in each strand. The nominal size of a finished wire rope is

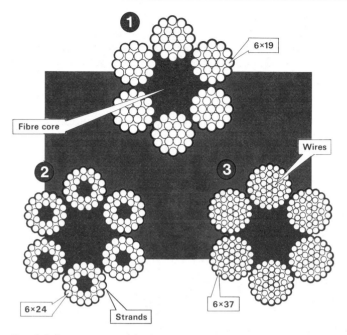

Fig. 9.3 Cross section of wire ropes with six strands round a fibre core.
(17 6 × 19; (2) 6 × 24; (3) 6 × 37.

usually expressed in terms of is circumference, but approximate
diameters are often used.

## 6 Plaited rope

Reference has been made in par. 4(a) above to yarns being laid
up to form a plaited rope. Size for size, plaited rope is less strong
than ordinary hawser-laid rope, but it possesses the advantage of
being more flexible and less likely to kink or twist. Plaiting or
braiding of yarn may be carried out in two ways:

(1) a solid braid (Fig. 9.1(1)) in which the yarns are twisted back
    and around each other; and

(2) known as *true-plaited rope* (Fig. 9.4(2)) in which the yarns
    are over-lapped progressively as, for example, when plaiting
    a girl's hair.

It is generally accepted that a solid-braided rope is weaker than a
true-plaited one, and the former is not used in the fire service.

Plaited rope is also made up with a central core. In the past
the core acted as a former only and did not take any of the load
on the rope; a cored rope was, therefore, less strong than an

uncored one of the same size. In some plaited rope formerly in use by fire brigades, the core was made up from short pieces which proved unsatisfactory because they tended to *waist* under load. A true-plaited 58 mm uncored rope made from Italian hemp has in the past been used as a turntable ladder rescue line. It had a breaking load of between 1·27 to 1·52 tonne and proved satisfactory in service. With the use of man-made fibres for rope-making, however, the quality of plaited rope has improved and BS 3367 provides for a cored plaited rope in polyester fibre (Fig. 9.5). This rope has an inner plait which contains a continuous

Fig. 9.4 (1): a solid-braided rope; (2) true-plaited rope.

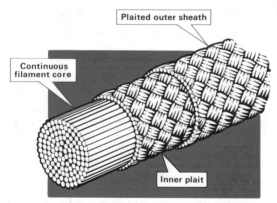

Plaited outer sheath

Continuous filament core

Inner plait

Fig. 9.5 Plaited polyester fibre rope constructed to British Standard 3367.

filament core of parallel yarns having a minimum breaking load of 2·4 tonne which, with a plaited sheath as an outer cover, provides a finished rope having a breaking load of over 4·05 tonne.

# Chapter 10
# Deterioration of rope

It is usual for purchasers of rope to obtain from the manufacturers a test certificate with each new consignment, the tests being defined in the specification to which the rope is made, and the certificate is usually only valid when the rope is new. After first usage, some form of deterioration may be present in a line; it may have suffered abrasion, for instance, or have been stored wet or contaminated with acid or alkali, and consequently the breaking load may be reduced. Other things being equal, the higher the initial breaking load, the longer the life that may be expected after a line has been put into use.

Throughout its life, rope will deteriorate to a greater or lesser extent according to the use, care and maintenance given it. Many of the causes of deterioration show early signs which will be revealed by careful examination. Such examinations should be made periodically, particularly in the case of lines used for rescue purposes, and are usually carried out at the same time as any load test to which the line is subjected.

## 1 Mechanical deterioration

This can be caused either through external abrasion or breakdown of the internal fibres, usually associated with the working of a rope on pulleys or bits too small in diameter. Lines should be uncoiled carefully to avoid kinking, and the end to be used should be uncoiled in an anti-clockwise direction. On no account should a load be applied to a line which still shows signs of kinking. If kinks do form, they should be carefully taken out before the line has become strained (see also Chapter 12, 'The use of lines').

Sharp bends should be avoided, particularly when securing the end of a line. When lowering a weight, the line must not be allowed to chafe on a sharp edge such as a coping. Dragging along the ground drives grit into the fibres and subsequent internal movement between the strands will cause the grit to cut into the fibres and seriously weaken them. If a line becomes very dirty it should be washed and allowed to dry in the same way as for canvas hose. When a line must change direction under load, it should be passed through a pulley block, but the sheave of the block must be sufficiently large to accommodate the line so that it does not ride on the shoulders. If the sheave is too narrow, more damage may be done than if a block had not been used. A line should not if possible be led round bends when under load but should be so arranged that as direct a pull as possible is obtained. When sharply bent under load the total stress is unevenly distributed amongst the individual fibres and hence the line is weakened.

## 2 Chemical deterioration

Chemical deterioration, particularly in natural fibre rope, may be caused by exposure to acids, alkalis or weather conditions, or by submersion in water for any considerable time. Therefore lines should be stored, as far as possible, in a cool dry place with plenty of ventilation. They should never be stored damp, or mildew will set in; nor should they be stored directly on the floor, but on boards raised above ground level. The coils should be turned over from time to time. The ideal temperature of a rope is between 13° and 21°C, with a humidity of between 40 and 65 per cent. Rope, like hose, is more liable to damage when wet, therefore, as far as possible, it should be kept dry, particularly when in use.

All fibres, whether vegetable or synethetic, are affected by temperature, the effects varying with the length and degree of exposure. Vegetable fibres exposed to dry heat lose their natural moisture content, the fibres becoming hard and brittle and the tensile strength of the rope is lowered. However, provided cordage is not heated to its charring temperature, it recovers some of the tensile strength lost due to heat.

### a. Natural fibre

The higher the grade of fibre used in the rope, the less is the detrimental effect of damp and moisture; consequently the expectation of life is higher for a better grade rope than for one of a poor quality. Rope is sometimes treated with stockholm tar (obtained from wood) to prevent mildew due to damp. This may be effected by introducing the tar into the fibre before spinning or subsequently, after the rope is made up, by boiling. The latter method weakens the rope and tarred ropes are always considered to have a lower breaking load than untreated ones.

Wet or damp lines should not be thrown on to the ground and left there, as this will cause the fibre to rot. Frequently the rot commences from the inside of the rope and cannot be detected by external examination; therefore the greatest care should be taken to avoid contamination of this description. Lines which have become wet should be dried out naturally, for if they are dried artifically and too rapidly, the fibres become brittle and the rope loses strength. They should not be kept in bright sunlight, as the rays of the sun produce an action which discolours the fibres and weakens them. They should never be left in contact with iron since rust is a potent cause of deterioration. Most acids and alkalis will cause burning and will destroy the strength and shorten the life of the fibre. Even fumes in certain cases have this effect.

## b. Man-made fibre

Man-made fibre rope is, however, less affected by chemical deterioration, and is free from attack by rot or mildew, although mildew may grow on surface impurities if such rope is stored wet or in damp conditions. Nylon and terylene are resistant to attack by oils and oxidising agents; nylon particularly is generally resistant to alkalis and weak concentrations of acid, and terylene is resistant to acids and weak concentrations of alkalis.

Deterioration of man-made fibres starts at temperatures above about 200°C and at somewhat lower temperatures if the exposure is of long duration. Man-made fibres are non-flammable, but will melt at a temperature of about 250°C, and man-made rope subjected to this temperature will part almost immediately. As the ignition temperature of natural fibres is of the same order, there is little difference between the effects on the two subtances at this temperature range.

# 3 Causes of deterioration

The following notes on the main causes of deterioration likely to occur to fire brigade lines, together with the signs by which they may be recognised, are given for guidance when inspecting lines.

## a. Mechanical deterioration

(1) External wear

This is caused by dragging over rough surfaces, window sills, etc. In extreme cases the strands become worn, their outer faces are flattened and the yarns are broken. During use some breakage of the outer fibres is unavoidable and, if not too extensive, will have little effect on the strength of the rope. Superficial abrasion of man-made fibre cordage may appear to take place easily, but this is relatively harmless as it not only forms a protective buffer to the inner filaments, but also enhances the handling qualities of the rope.

(2) Internal wear

This is caused by repeated kinking and by dragging along the ground, which forces grit into the fibres. Subsequent internal movement between the strands causes the grit to cut the fibres and weaken them. Internal wear may be indicated by excessive looseness of the strands and yarns.

### (3) Local abrasion

This is caused by the line being passed over sharp or rough edges while under load. The yarns or strands may be torn intermittently throughout the line, and although slight damage to the fibres may be harmless (see (1) above), serious damage to one strand or lesser damage to more than one strand should be considered harmful to the line.

### (4) Cuts, contusions, etc

These may be caused by falling debris or by careless use. The line may be damaged both internally and externally. Damage may be indicated by flattening, or by local breaking or loosening of the strands or yarns (see also (1) and (2) above).

## b. Chemical deterioration

### (1) Chemical attack

This is caused by exposure to acids and alkalis in concentrated form, as vapour (such as might be given off by vehicle batteries) or from some industrial processes. Sulphur dioxide gas is extremely detrimental to rope, particularly if the rope becomes wet after exposure to the fumes as is likely at fires at oil refineries. Solvent cleaners may remove the natural oils from vegetable fibres and organic substances may cause deterioration of synthetic fibres. Chemical attack may be indicated by softening of the materials so that the surface fibres may be rubbed off, often as a powder.

### (2) Mildew

Rotting of fibres is generally caused by the effects of mildew due to lines being stored wet or damp. Mildew causes loss of strength; externally the fibres may be found to break easily, but internally it is difficult to detect. Extreme cases may be recognised by the characteristic mouldy smell. When lines become wet they should be dried naturally, as too much heat will cause the fibres to become brittle and weaken. Mildew does not attack man-made fibres, although it may grow on surface impurities if lines are stored in a wet and dirty condition. Discoloration of the fibres may occur.

### (3) Heat

Damage by heat may be caused during use or storage, and in extreme cases charring, singeing and fusing of the fibres may occur. All these may be readily seen during inspection.

### (4) Sunlight

Lines will deteriorate from prolonged exposure to bright sunlight. In extreme cases bleaching occurs, and the fibres become brittle; manila and sisal rope are particularly affected by this.

## 4 Deterioration of wire rope

Wire rope may be considered as being liable to deterioration in a similar manner to fibre rope. It is particularly important that a kinked wire rope should not be subjected to a load, as once a kink is formed, it cannot be removed, and the strength of the rope is permanently impaired. Both the steel wire and the fibre core are liable to chemical attack, and if the rope is left wet and unprotected from the weather, rust may affect the wire and mildew damage the core.

During manufacture wire rope is fully lubricated (including the fibre core) to reduce friction between the wires and to prevent corrosion by excluding moisture. To maintain this protection in service, cable should be treated with a thin coating of petroleum jelly.

Cables will weaken through normal wear, which is usually apparent to the eye when outside strands of the cable assume a smooth and polished appearance. The most important cause of weakening in a cable, however, is the fracture of individual wires, generally referred to as *needling*. This is most likely to occur where a cable is subjected to repeated flexing; the part of the cable most likely to be affected in this way is that portion which winds round a drum. The number of wires per strand is obviously important in assessing the degree of weakening in a cable through needling, and it is interesting to note as a general guide that in factory legislation, the Building (Safety, Health and Welfare) Regulations, 1948, Part III, Clause (58(2), provide that:

'No wire rope shall be used in raising or lowering or as a means of suspension if in any length of ten diameters the total number of visible broken wires exceeds five per cent of the total number of wires in the rope'.

In a rope with 37 wires per strand, five per cent of the total number amounts to about 11; for a rope with 24 wires per strand, the figure is 7; and for one with 12 wires per strand the figure is only 4. So that even with only 12 wires per strand these Regulations permit 4 broken wires in 10 diameters, which is a length of about 150 mm on a 16 mm diameter rope.

The general practice in the fire service is to replace cables when general needling is apparent over much of their length, which is long before they reach the condition described above, and the *Fire Service Drill Book* requires that in any case the number of broken wires should not be allowed to exceed one half the number permitted in the Regulations quoted above. This is two and a half per cent of the total number of wires in the rope.

# Chapter 11
# Lines used in the fire service

Cordage forms an essential part of fire brigade equipment. There is hardly an operation in fire fighting whether it be effecting a rescue, getting a length of hose up a building or making fast the suction when working from open water, which does not call for the use of a line of one type or another. The lines mentioned below will be found in general use on the majority of fire brigade appliances throughout the country.

## 1 Specifications

British Standard 2052 deals with the construction of rope made from coir, hemp, manila and sisal for general purposes, incuding lifting blocks, slings, tackles, etc. In the foreword it states:

'For new ropes employed for lifting purposes, a ratio of maximum dead working load to minimum breaking load of the rope of not less than six is recommended as a factor of safety. The factor of safety employed should be considered together with the purpose for which the rope is used, the conditions of service and the condition of the rope; and as so defined, while six is recommended as a minimum for new ropes used under the most favourable conditions, it is in most cases desirable to increase this factor to eight for fibre rope slings in order to make arbitrary allowance for the unavoidable increase of stress at the bight, and where the rope passes around the body of the crane, hook, etc.'

British Standard 3367 is a specification for fire brigade rescue lines. It was prepared at the request of the Local Authorities Standards Advisory Committee of the British Standards Institution and, together with BS 2052, was subsequently recommended for fire brigade use by the Central Fire Brigades Advisory Councils. The Standard includes the general construction of the rope from which the lines are made, details of the make-up of lowering and turntable ladder rescue lines together with guy and tail lines, and of line terminations. The Standard requires that the rope from which these lines are constructed shall be of 3-strand hawser-laid Italian hemp having a minimum breaking strain of 2·85 tonne or 3-strand hawser-laid polyester fibre (terylene) having a minimum breaking load of 4·05 tonne. Provision is also made for a cored plaited rope of polyester fibre which also has the same minimum breaking load (see page 102). Rope of this construction may be used for both lowering and rescue lines.

With regard to wire rope used on wheeled escapes, 13.5 m extension ladders and turntable ladders, and fibre rope on other extension ladders, the appropriate JCDD Specifications contain recommendations as to breaking loads and include references to the British Standards concerned with thimbles, splices, etc., and to the diameter of the sheaves and drums over which the cables run.

The specifications prepared by the Committee on Uniform and Personal Equipment (like the Joint Committee on Design and Development, a Committee of the Central Fire Brigades Advisory Councils), includes one for belt or pocket lines.

A handy guide to the use of rope, particularly in connection with lifting tackle, is published by the Cordage Manufacturers Institute 79 Queens Rd, Southend-on-Sea SS1 1PY, entitled: 'Lifting Tackle—Schedule and Code of Practice to assist users to comply with the provisions of the Factories Act'.

## 2 Rescue lines (turntable ladders)

These are special extra-long lines used for rescue work with turntable ladders (Fig. 11.1). The length may vary with the type of ladder on which the line is carried, but generally it is 67 m in length and is constructed from 50 mm hawser-laid Italian hemp, or from 50 mm hawser-laid or plaited polyester fibre.

One end of the line is fitted with a thimble and a ring to which is attached a steel snap hook (a). Before the line is made up it is rove through a galvanised iron sheave (b), which is then drawn to the end of the line until it rests against the thimble. The line is then generally coiled down on a wooden bollard (c) to which one end is permanently secured. Alternatively the line may be wound on a large wooden reel, the axis of which is extended at each end to form a handle. The free end of the line, with the hook and sheave, in the former case, is stowed in the centre of the coil where it is ready for immediate use. The line is carried on the appliance either in a clip behind the driver's seat, or, if the ladder is fitted with a revolving turntable platform, the bollard may be carried there.

Rescue lines bear identification markings near the free end, usually in the form of a copper rivet securing a washer on which is inscribed the date of issue and the station identity. This information is additional to that required on all lines made up to BS 3367, which states that a non-ferrous metal ferrule or a non-slip plastics sleeve is to be secured to the line on which is stamped the manufacturer's name, trade or other identification mark, the nominal size, the date of supply of the coil of rope from which the line was made and the BS number.

The use of rescue lines and of the canvas safety belt or sling (Fig. 11.1(d)) which comprises an essential part of the rescue equipment, is fully described in the *Manual, Book 5 Chapter 4 Turn-table Ladders'*

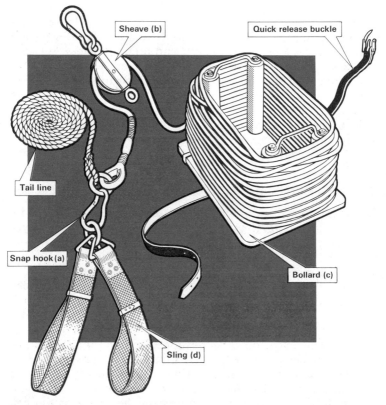

Fig. 11.1 View of a typical sling, spring, snap hook, sheave and wooden bollard for rescue line used with turntable ladders.

## 3 Lowering lines

In accordance with BS 3367, the standard length of a lowering line is 40 m, other lengths may be specified to meet local requirements. The lines are constructed of 50 mm hawser-laid Italain hemp or of 50 mm hawser-laid or plaited polyester fibre.

A lowering line should be made up with two legs at one end or, as an alternative if required, it may terminate in a snap hook with or without a swivel. With the former type (Fig. 11.2) each leg is fitted with a running eye, the lengths being so adjusted that the two bights permit of a body being placed in them and lowered. These legs are made by splicing in an additional 1·68 m approximately of line (a) about 1·5 m from one end. This provides two legs, the shorter of which (b) is the standing part and is indicated by a Turk's head knot (c) worked round it just below the splice, so that it can be readily identified by touch in the dark. The fact that one leg is shorter than the other allows the

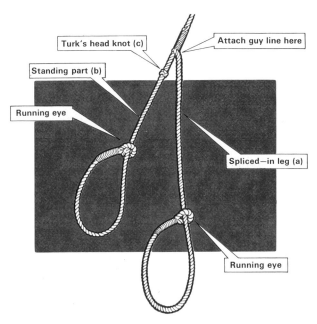

Fig. 11.2 Hawser-laid lowering line with spliced-in leg fitted with running eyes.

person being lowered to assume as comfortable a position as possible, with his head upright. It is important, therefore, that the shorter leg should be made from the standing part, as it is the end which is passed round the body under the arm-pits. If the shorter leg were made from the length spliced in, and the splice were to part, the person being lowered would be suspended head downwards by the standing part round his legs, and a serious accident might result. If on the other hand, the line is properly constructed and the splice gives, the person being lowered is still securely held, head uppermost.

Lowering lines, being primarily rescue lines, are often carried externally on the carriage of the escape, or some other accessible position. They are sometimes made up on a special leather cradle, or on a wooden bollard, but nowadays they are more generally stowed and carried in a canvas bag fitted with a carrying harness (see page 123). Whatever method is employed, a lowering line should always be made up and stowed so that it is ready for immediate use in any emergency. No line assigned to rescue work should normally be used for any other purpose. Lowering lines bear identification markings similar to the turntable ladder rescue lines. The use of lowering lines is fully described in the *Manual, Book 12 Chapter 1 'Rescue at fires'*.

## 4 Long lines

Long lines are general purpose lines, 30 m in length and 50 mm in circumference, usually made from untanned manila having plain whipped ends. They are used for a variety of purposes, the most common being to haul a length of hose aloft. They may also be found useful for the purpose of roping off streets or areas on the fireground to hold back spectators. They should not be used for rescue work except in an emergency when no lowering line is available.

Cordage Manufacturers Institutes handbook 'Lifting Tackle' previously referred to, recommends that where manila rope is used and human life is involved, a grade of rope not lower than BS 2052, Grade I, or its equivalent, should be used. Grade I ropes in this British Standard have a minimum breaking load of 2·03 tonnes in the 50 mm size.

## 5 Short lines

Short lines are normally 15·2 m in length and are usually made of 50 mm untanned manila identical with the long line describes above. Short lines may, however, be made by cutting out the sound parts from condemned lowering lines. Short lines of varying materials and length may, therefore, be found in use.

The short line is used for innumerable small jobs for which the long line would be unnecessarily cumbersome, the most common being to make fast the strainer and suction when working from open water. It is also usually more convenient for strengthening scaling ladders or lowering them into holds or basements, etc. as there is less line to pull clear at each stage of the operation.

## 6 Escape lines

An escape line is between 4·5 and 6 metres in length secured to the top round of an extension ladder or escape by means of a running eye, the free end of which is taken into the building to assist men to find their way back to the window from a smoke-laden room. It may also be used for securing the head of an extension ladder. There is no specified material or size for escape lines, but as they are commonly made from condemned lowering, long or short lines, they may generally be stated to be 50 mm lines made from either Italian hemp or untanned manila.

An escape line is often secured by means of an eye attached to the top round of escapes or extension ladders with a snap hook attached to the end for clipping the rope to itself when securing. When not in use it is coiled and secured by metal clips, but in some areas it is allowed to lie along the strings of the ladder where it is ready to hand at all times. When arranged in this way, care must be taken to see that it does not foul the extensions as they ride over one another when extending or lowering.

## 7 Guy lines

Guy lines which are in accordance with BS 3367 are normally 40 m in length and are made from No. 5 hemp sash cord or from plaited polyester fibre log-line of the same size with a minimum breaking load of 270 kilograms. They are used in conjunction with lowering lines and turntable ladder rescue lines. A guy line is thrown down and used by the man below to keep the person being rescued clear of the building while he or she is being lowered. Guy lines should also be used for this purpose when long lines are being used for rescue purposes.

When used with lowering lines, guy lines usually have both ends whipped, and may be permanently attached to the lowering line by means of a clove hitch, one half of which is made above and the other half below the splice on the standing part. Those with turntable ladder rescue lines usually have one end whipped and a thimble at the other end, which may be permanently attached to the ring on the rescue lines by means of a screwed shackle.

Guy lines used for steadying turntable ladders are dealt with in the *Manual, Book 5 Chapter 10 'Working with turntable ladders'*.

## 8 Bobbin lines

The bobbin line is a light line, 40 m in length, usually made from 900 g plaited cotton cord. It is used for hauling light gear aloft, or for bringing up a heavier line, and is attached to hook belts used in conjunction with hook ladders. There are two types in use, as under.

## a. Bobbin line

The bobbin line, which takes its name from the fact that it is wound on a leather bobbin (Fig. 11.3) rather like a cotton reel (a) is carried in a special pouch (b) on the hook belt, with the opening underneath, so that when the catch is released the weight of the bobbin causes the line to fall out into the fireman's hand ready for use.

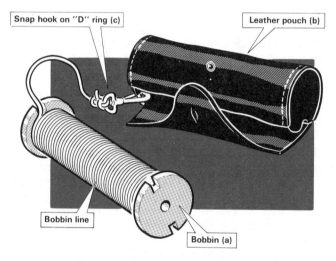

Fig. 11.3 Bobbin line and pouch as carried on a hook belt.

After the line is made up on the bobbin, the free end, which is fitted with a swivel and snap hook, is attached to a 'D' ring on the hook belt (c). One end of the line is thus always secured, so that the bobbin need only be cast away and the line will pay itself out, leaving both hands free for other work.

## b. Pouch line

This line is used with a special pouch designed to provide a more satisfactory and efficient method of carrying and throwing out the bobbin. When used with the pouch, the line is known as a 'pouch line'. The general design (Fig. 11.4) consists of a small detachable pouch to contain the standard bobbin line made up in the shape of a ball, a holding strap for securing the pouch to the safety belt, and a simple former to facilitate winding the line into the correct size.

The various parts consist of:

## (1) The pouch

A small leather pouch (a) is made to open out so that the bobbin line can be inserted when wound in a ball. The pouch has raised side rims (b) to prevent lateral displacement from the holding strap, and press studs (c) for closing the sides. A white strip (d) is sometimes sewn round the outer circumference of the pouch to aid speedy location in the dark, and a 'D' ring is sewn inside to which one end of the bobbin line is permanently attached.

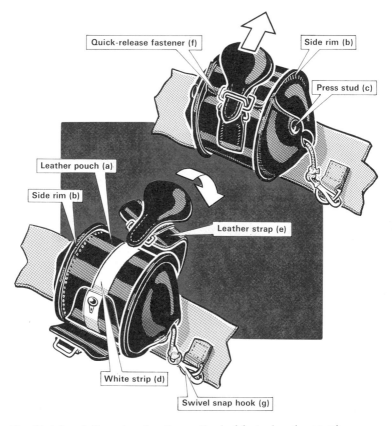

Fig. 11.4 Pouch line, showing the method of fastening the pouch.

## (2) Holding strap

A leather strap (e), 75 mm wide to fit between the rims on the pouch and provided with a quick-release fastener (f), is permanently riveted to the hook belt and holds the pouch in position.

## (3) Line

The line is the standard bobbin line of 40 m of plaited cord. One end is secured to the 'D' ring inside the pouch and a small swivel snap hook (g) is attached to the other end.

## (4) Former

The former (Fig. 11.5), on which the bobbin line is wound to form a convenient ball, is a short length of dowel rod (a) 19 mm in diameter, through which holes are drilled to take two movable crossbars of dowel rod (b), 6 mm in diameter. Experiments have shown that the dimensions of the line former as given in Fig. 11.5 are the most suitable for producing the correct size of a ball.

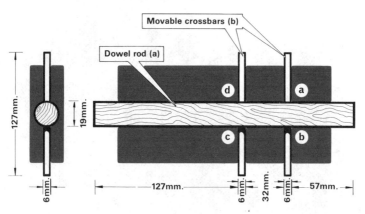

Fig. 11.5 The former on which the bobbin line is wound.

## (5) Winding the line

To wind the line into a suitable ball, the free end, i.e. the end to which the snap hook is attached, is held at 'c' and the line is wound round the former in groups of ten turns each, in the sequence 'ca, cb, bd and da', finishing off to complete as symmetrical a ball as possible. This leaves the snap hook leading from the centre of the ball, the other end being attached to the 'D' ring inside the pouch. The ball is released from the former by withdrawing the two cross bars and sliding it off the main rod. It can then be placed in the pouch; the pouch is fastened up and secured to the hook belt, and the snap hook is attached to the 'D' ring on the hook belt.

(6) Method of use

By releasing the fastener of the holding strap, the pouch containing the line comes completely away from the hook belt. The pouch can then be thrown or dropped as required, the method of winding the pouch line permitting it to run out easily from the centre (in the same way as a ball of string) without kinking or hindrance. With a little practice this pouch can be thrown upward or forward, e.g., into a window or across a gap between buildings, the line running freely in the same manner as a rocket line. (The rocket line is described in the *Manual, Part 7: Chapter 1, 'Fireboats and their Equipment'*).

## 9 Tail lines

A tail line is between 4·5 and 6 m in length, is usually made of 38 mm manila rope and is kept permanently secured of the turntable ladder rescue sling (see Fig. 11.1). It is sometimes referred to as a *guy line*. The tail line is taken into a building with the rescue sling and is used to steady a person being lowered as the ladder is trained away from the building.

## 10 Belt lines

These are in general use by fire brigades and are commonly 3·6 m in length, but their exact length and composition may vary. Lines made to the Uniform and Personal Equipment Specification are made of 3-ply cabled cord 12-strand 60-thread hemp rope yarn having a weight of 2·2 kg per 90 m with a breaking load of not less than 210 kg.

Belt lines are used for a wide variety of purposes, including lashing branches, etc. The belt line, as its name implies, is usually carried on the fireman's belt, made up in a *blood knot,* as describes on page 128 in Chapter 12. The line should be worn on the left side of the belt, between the buckle and axe-pouch. Alternatively, it may be carried in the tunic pocket, in which case it is sometimes known locally as a *pocket line.*

## 11 Guide lines

Guide lines are used when necessary when breathing apparatus is worn, and the term 'guide line' means a special line which may be used either as a *main guide line* or alternatively as a *branch guide line* when it is necessary to traverse or search deeply off a main guide line. The use of guide lines is fully described in the 'Operational Procedure for use with Breathing Apparatus, Section III (see the *Manual, Book 6 Chapter 12*).

A guide line (Fig. 11.6) should be 60 m in length, between 19 to 25 mm circumference, and may be hawser-laid or plaited

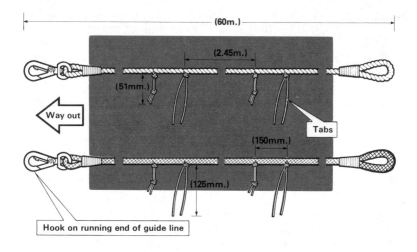

Fig. 11.6 Guide lines, showing the terminations and the means of identifying the line by touch.

construction. The running end terminates with a snap hook and the other end with a loop 150 mm in length; a guide line can thus be extended by clipping on the snap hook of another line. The hook should be smaller and different from the snap hook on the personal line (see Fig. 11.7), but sufficiently large enough to hook on to another guide line.

The purpose of a guide line is to provide a means whereby under certain conditions the first team or crew to enter and search a smoke-filled risk can retrace their steps, or to enable subsequent teams or crews to make their way to the scene of operations and return as necessary without difficulty. In order to identify the line itself, and to recognise by touch the 'way out', two tabs 150 mm apart are fitted at 2·45 m intervals along the whole length of the line. One tab has two separate knots and an overall length of 50 mm; the other is unknotted and is 125 mm long. The knotted tab is on the WAY OUT side of the plain tab, i.e. nearer the running end of the line which terminates with the snap hook.

The line is carried stowed in a container, the looped end of the line being attached to a snap hook inside the container. It is important when the line is being stowed that the looped end is always secured inside the container and the stowage so arranged that the running end pays out first. When in use the line is secured by means of the snap hook at some convenient point at the breathing apparatus control and, with this arrangement, the shorter knotted tabs are always on the correct side.

## 12 Personal lines

As with guide lines, personal lines and their use are fully described in Section III of the 'Operational Procedure' in the *Manual, Book 6, Chapter 12, Sub-section 4*. The term 'personal line' means a special line secured to a breathing apparatus set, and which may be attached to a guide line to enable the wearer to follow the line and search off it up to the limit of the length of the personal line.

Personal lines (Fig. 11.7) should be 6·10 m in length and about 12·5 mm circumference, but no special construction is specified.

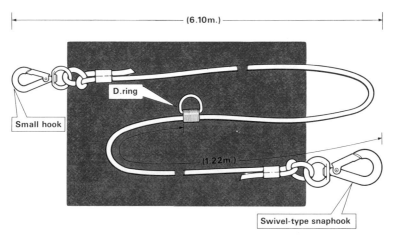

Fig. 11.7 The personal line showing terminations and 'D' ring.

The running end terminates with a swivel-type snap hook of a size large enough to allow it to be clipped on to the guide line and traverse freely along it. The other end of the line is fitted with a smaller hook for attaching to the harness of a breathing apparatus set. A 'D' ring is fitted to the personal line at a distance of 1·22 m from the running end, and is provided to permit the use of a 'short line' when a guide line is being followed.

The personal line should be stowed in a pouch-type container (Fig. 11.8) attached to the harness (belt) of a breathing apparatus set. It will be seen from Fig. 11.8 that the pouch has three pockets, the largest at the rear for stowing the 4·9 m of the line, one at the front for stowing the 1·22 m section of the line, and the smallest for stowing the hook on the running end of the line. The 'D' ring on the line is attached to a press button secured to a tab

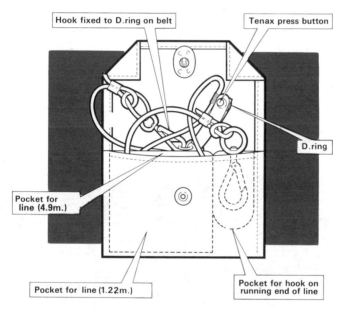

Fig. 11.8 Diagram of pouch suitable for carrying a personal line showing the arrangement of the pockets.

which in turn is secured to a 'D' ring on the belt. The snap hook at the end of the 4·9 m length of line is also attached to this 'D' ring. The line is therefore stowed with the 'short line' ready for use, the full length being obtained when required by actuating the press button to release the 'D' ring on the line.

## 13 Coir, or grass, lines

Grass lines are in 219 metre lengths and are used on fireboats. They are usually made of coir, which owing to its lightness, floats on the surface of the water and is therefore ideal for use on river craft. The ends of the line are spliced together to make an endless whip, which is used for hauling lengths of hose ashore. The line is passed round bollards or through pulley blocks placed one forward and one aft, and the bight is taken ashore. Hose can then be brought either to the shore or to the boat by hauling on the line. It is of interest to note that BS 2052 indicates a minimum breaking load of 355 kg hawser-laid coir rope as compared with 2·03 tonnes for a similar size in Grade I manila, and states that coir ropes should not be used under any circumstances for lifting purposes.

A variety of warps (mooring lines) are used on fireboats. No standard lengths or measurements can be given, and it is usual for coils of various sizes to be issued and cut as required. Manila, hemp, coir and occasionally cotton lines of all sizes from 12·5 to 100 mm circumference, and any length from 3 to 12 metres will therefore be found for mooring river craft. Lines used on fireboats are not made up on bollards, but are coiled down either on the deck or in lockers.

Whilst considerable variation in the types of line in use may occur, the majority fall into one or other of the above categories, though differences in material, lengths and methods of making up may be encountered. Increasing use, however, is being made of synthetic ropes for marine purposes, including those made of polyproplene, which is rot-proof, floats on water and is resistant to acids and alkalis. Synthetic ropes of one type or another will be found on many river craft.

# Chapter 12
# The making-up, use and testing of lines

## 1 The making-up of lines

It is essential that lines, especially those used for rescue, should be securely made up for carrying, yet they must be instantly available for use when required. It is important also that the line should pay out freely when cast down from an upper floor, or when pulled out. When made up, lowering and long lines should be convenient for carrying up a ladder, and should have no loose ends to become entangled in the rounds of the ladder. If a line carrier is not used, the line must be made up in such a way that the coils do not lie across the fireman's chest when the line is slung over his shoulder.

There is probably no single method making up lines that completely satisfies all fire brigade requirements, but the one

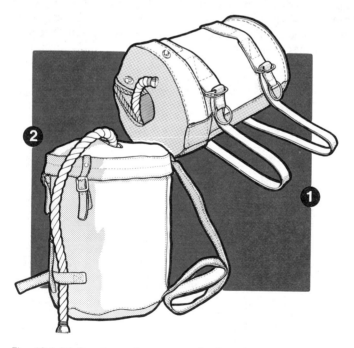

Fig. 12.1 (1) One type of canvas carrier for a long line. (2) Another type which is designed to be carried in a vertical position.

favoured by the majority of brigades in this country is to use a canvas bag type of carrier in which to stow the line, and which is fitted with a carrying harness. Other methods include lines made up in a carrying harness, and some of these are described below.

## a. Canvas line carriers

Canvas carriers for long lines (Fig. 12.1) are usually cylindrical in shape, although some may be found which are rectangular. All types are designed to be secured to the fireman's back by a shoulder harness consisting of two adjustable straps generally fitted with quick-release buckles, thus leaving the arms free when working with ladders. The line carrier shown in Fig. 12.1(1) is approximately 380 mm in length, 250 mm in diameter and is made of canvas. The hinged lid is secured with three turn-button fastenings and has a section cut away to facilitate the extraction of the line. The type shown in Fig. 12.1(2) is similar in construction but is designed to be carried in a vertical position.

The lowering line carrier Fig. 12.2(1) is of similar construction to the long line carrier shown in Fig. 12.1(1); it is 460 mm in length, 230 mm in diameter but has an external pocket in which

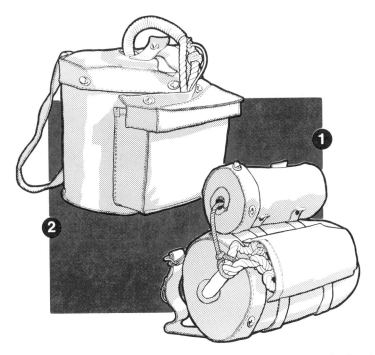

Fig. 12.2 (1) Canvas lowering line carrier with a separate carrier for the guy line. (2) Another type in which both the lowering line legs and the guy lines are stowed in a pocket on the carrier.

to stow the lowering line legs. The guy line is carried in a smaller carrier, 330 mm in length, 125 mm in diameter, which is secured by four press studs to the webbing harness above the main carrier. When worn the main carrier should fit in the small of the back with the pocket carrying the lowering line legs on the underside of the main carrier and the guy line carrier secured on the shoulder harness above. In the carrier in Fig. 12.2(2) there is no separate carrier for the guy line; both the legs of the lowering line and the guy line are stowed in the pocket of the carrier.

The method of stowing the lines in the container varies. One method utilises a line former, such as a broomstick, and the line is wound neatly round the stick from bottom to top so that the line resembles a ball of string. The line is then placed in the carrier and the stick is withdrawn. However, the method generally favoured by brigades is not to coil the line systematically at all, but merely to stow it with the minimum amount of care necessary to obviate kinks and looped turns. On the completion of the stowage of a long line, about 100 mm of the free end of the line is left protruding from the cut-away portion of the lid. When using the long line aloft, the protruding end is firmly grasped and the carrier containing the remainder of the line is thrown clear of the building. It will be found that as the carrier falls to the ground, the line will pay out freely. At ground level the turn button securing the lid is released and the remainder of the line may be extracted for use.

The lowering line is stowed in the carrier free end first, with the leg splice on the standing part leading through the aperture in the lid, and the two legs are stowed in the exterior pocket. The guy line is stowed either in the separate carrier or in the pocket with one end secured to the standing part of the lowering line in the normal manner. When using the lowering line, the carrier is placed in a convenient position on the floor of the building, the small carrier, if used, is unclipped from the harness and the carrier with the guy line is thrown clear of the building to ground level. If no guy line carrier is used, the guy line is removed from the pocket and is thrown clear of the building to the ground below. The lowering line legs are removed from the pocket and sufficient length of line is withdrawn from the carrier to enable the line to be got to work. The remainder of the line will pay out from the carrier as the rescue takes place.

If natural fibre lines are kept stowed in canvas bags, they should be removed from the bags at regular intervals, inspected for signs of mildew and thoroughly aired. Natural fibre lines should not be replaced in the canvas bag if they are wet; they should be made up on the fireground in a figure of eight (see par. (b) below) for return to the station, where they should be thoroughly dried before restowing. Canvas bags should also be completely dry before lines are stowed in them.

Although moisture has no deleterious effect on man-made fibre lines, it is preferable not to replace them when wet in the canvas bag, as the bags must never be stowed away on an appliance when they are wet.

### b. Figure-of-eight

The figure-of-eight method of making up a line is simple, quick and undoubtedly the best for making up lines on the fireground, especially if the lines are wet, but it has the disadvantage that the line may easily become loose and is liable to become entangled with other gear in the appliance locker.

A line is made up in figure-of-eight by holding one end of the line in the right hand, then holding the hands at a suitable distance apart, and laying the line over and under each hand. (Fig. 12.3).

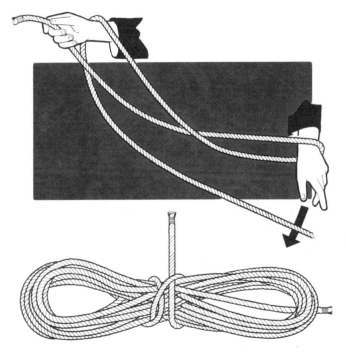

Fig. 12.3 Method of making up a line by means of a figure-of-eight.

This operation is easier if carried out by two men, but it can be done single-handed quite simply by dipping each hand under the line in turn. To obviate kinking, the line should preferably be laid out straight on the ground. When made up the line is secured by putting a clove hitch round the centre of the figure-of-eight.

This method of making up is not very satisfactory on its own when the line has to be carried up an escape or ladder, since the coils of a line must never lie across the chest as they will if the line is slung over the shoulder in bandolier fashion. If a tidy stow is desired, a line made up in figure-of-eight should be secured in a harness fitted with quick-release buckles and having carrying straps (Fig. 12.4(1)). Both the lowering and the guy line should

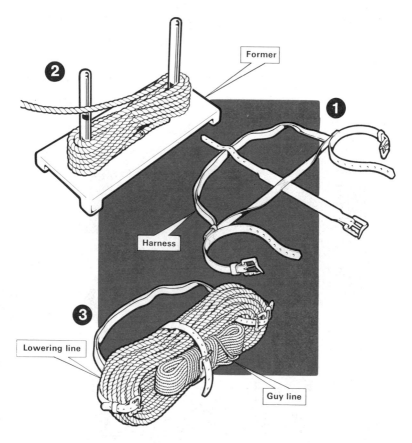

Fig. 12.4 (1) Quick-release harness for carrying a lowering line. (2) A former for making up a lowering line in a figure-of-eight. (3) A lowering line made up with the guy line and strapped in the harness for carrying.

be made up carefully, preferably on a former (Fig. 12.4(2)), of such a pattern that the arms can be adjusted in width to enable the guy line to be made up to a smaller size so that it will lie neatly in the centre of the lowering line (Fig. 12.4(3)).

The line should be laid on the floor where it is required to be got to work, the harness should be released and the legs and guy line withdrawn. The guy line should then be thrown clear of the building to the ground below. When the lowering legs have been placed on the person to be lowered the remainder of the line will pay out quite freely from the position where it has been laid.

### c. Other methods of making up lines
Another method of making up lowering and long lines is the normal circular coil (Fig. 12.5) where the line is formed into a coil about 460 mm in diameter. Like the figure-of-eight, this is

End made fast

Fig. 12.5 To coil a line for running.

easy to make and the line pays out freely, but when made up the line is not so convenient for carrying unless it is contained on a special harness. Most other methods require the use of special formers and bollards, and when made up the line is generally contained in a harness with quick-release buckles. Another method incorporates loops (the American rope coil, or similar) and this is very much like the method employed for making up pocket or belt lines, i.e. the blood knot (see par. (e) below), except that the loops are carried to the ends of the coil. In use the arms are passed through the loops and the line is carried on the back.

### d. Making up turntable ladder rescue lines
Rescue lines for turntable ladders do not under normal conditions have to be carried up the ladder, and by virtue of their extra long

length, they require a secure method of making up, yet the line must be free to pay out as the ladder is extended. Although the canvas bag container is used by some brigades, the cradle is more widely used, and this has been illustrated in Chapter 11 (Fig. 11.1).

The line is made up right-handed (i.e. in a clockwise direction) on the cradle working outwards from the bollards in layers consisting of three coils side by side. The first layer is placed on the cradle platform and the following layers are continued by crossing the line to the centre to each new layer. To ensure an even lay, when the line is crossed to the centre it is advanced from on bollard to the next. Making up should continue to the last 6 m approximately of line, which should be flaked in the well formed by the line passing round the four bollards, together with the rescue sling, tail line and guy line (if fitted). This 6 m of line is sufficient to enable the rescue sling to be taken to the head of the turntable ladder whilst the cradle remains on the ground at the offside rear of the appliance (see the *Manual, Book 5, Part 3, Chapter 4 'General information on turntable ladders'*. The rescue line is finally secured to the cradle by means of a leather harness, which is fitted with quick-release buckles.

### e. Making up pocket or belt lines

Pocket or belt lines should be made up in a *blood knot* (Fig. 12.6), the object of which is to make up the line in such a form that whilst it is quite firm, it is not tied and can be easily and

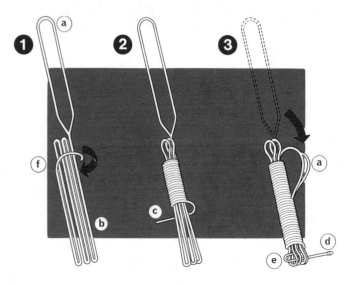

Fig. 12.6 Method of making up a belt line by means of a blood knot.

quickly released when required. The loop provided is used to secure the line to a fireman's belt, if worn. Neatness and correctness in making this knot can only be achieved by each individual fireman experimenting with his own line, as belt lines are of varying lengths.

A loop (a) about 175 mm long is made at one end of the line (Fig. 12.6(1)), or, if an eye splice is fitted, this may be employed. With the remainder of the line a coil (b) is now made, the same length as the loop, leaving spare a length of line (c) sufficient to bind the whole coil. The coil (b) is now bound with the line (c). After approximately half the coil has been bound in this way (Fig. 12.6(2)), the loop (a) is folded back down on the coil and the binding is continued (Fig. 12.6(3)) both round the coil and the loop until the end is nearly reached. If the length of the line (c) has been accurately calculated a short length (d) should be left which is doubled back on itself and pushed through the loop (e) at the end of the coil. The knot is then tightened from the opposite end by pulling tightly on the visible portion of the loop (a), the other end of the loop thus clamping the end (d). To release the knot, the end (d) is merely pulled out and the line will then pay out.

It is necessary to practise tying this knot so as to be able to estimate how much free end must be left for binding after the completion of the coil. It is helpful to mark the line with a piece of coloured cotton, shown at (f) in Fig. 12.6(1) when the correct length has been determined.

## 2 The use of lines

It has already been stressed that great care must be taken of lines, as it is obvious that the strength of any line is only equal to that of its weakest part. If a line must be passed over any sharp edge during its course, e.g. a window ledge, wall or coping, some simple protection such as a sack, mat or even a wooden hose ramp should always be used to prevent chafing.

When taking a new coil of rope into use, the bottom inside end should be taken out first and, if this has not already been done, the line should be stretched (by carrying out the standard test); the ends should then be whipped or crowned. After use a line should be cleaned and dried before being made up and stowed on an appliance.

It cannot be too strongly emphasised that a line must always be kept free from knots and kinks. Kinks are formed by twists in the line, and when signs of twisting are apparent, or a kink has actually formed, the line should be lightly gripped in the left hand and should be pulled through this grip by the right hand, allowing the free end of the line to untwist (Fig. 12.7). Twists and kinks should never be forcibly removed as this is liable to cause incipient damage, and it is therefore important to ensure that the line is free from twists and kinks before the standard test is applied.

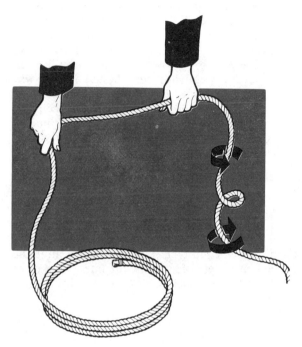

Fig. 12.7 Removing the twists from a line.

Cordage is very resilient and will absorb a number of turns in its length without becoming snarled if the length is sufficient and if the turns correspond with the lay of the rope; if the turns are against the lay, however, the line will quickly become snarled. For this reason lines of right-hand lay (and this applies to most fire brigade lines) must always be coiled down right-handed, whilst ropes of left-hand lay must be coiled down left-handed.

When coiling down a line that has the end made fast (see Fig. 12.5) coiling should start close to where the standing part is made fast, and each loop should be laid flat upon the one below until the end is reached. Coiling will be made easier if the line is first laid out as straight as possible along the ground. The running part is now underneath the coil, so the coil should be turned over; the line should now run out freely when required. The running part or end should always be on top of any coil.

To coil a small line (right-hand lay) in the hand (Fig. 12.8), the line should be held in the right hand with the thumb pointing towards the line end, and when coiling in the left hand, the left thumb should point towards the bight. The coil will then form correctly.

A line which may have to be paid out quickly should be flaked down in as long flakes as space allows. When flaked, a line does not acquire as many turns as when it is coiled, and it will therefore run out with less chance of becoming snarled. Care should be taken to see that each turn at the end of a flake is laid over that immediately preceding it to ensure that the upper turns are given no opportunity to catch in the lower turns as the line runs out.

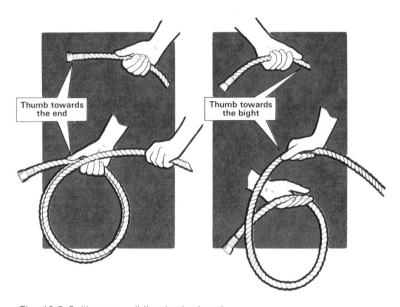

Fig. 12.8 Coiling a small line in the hand.

# 3 Standard tests and examination

All lines, from whatever material they are made, should be handled with the greatest of care, and proper examination and maintenance are essential if the lines are to be kept in good serviceable condition.

## a. Testing of lines

Fire brigade lines should be tested at the times specified and in accordance with the *Fire Service Drill Book*.

## b. Examination of lines

The load applied to lines in the standard tests will not necessarily give a true indication of their condition, as deterioration in its early stages may not be sufficient at the time of the test to affect the strength. On completion of the test, therefore, it is important that the line should be carefully examined for evidence of deterioration, and that whippings, splicings and fittings, such as swivels, snap hooks, etc., are free from defect. The examination should be carried out at the times specified and in accordance with the *Fire Service Drill Book*.

It is not possible to define a standard of acceptance or rejection of a line as a result of this examination, as there is no clear-cut boundary between those lines which are safe and those which are not. The decision as to whether a line should be scrapped or its use continued must be based on an assessment of its general condition as revealed by the examination and on the result of the load test applied. This is particularly important for lines used for rescue purposes, and lines showing signs of excessive wear or deterioration should be withdrawn from service. In any case, it is general practice in the fire service to withdraw rescue liens after eights years' use. If still satisfactory at the end of this period, rescue lines on being withdrawn are generally put to other uses, such as for short lines, escape lines and hose whips.

It might be expected that lines made from man-made fibres would have a longer life than those made from natural fibres, but insufficient experience is available at present to indicate the potential life of a rescue line made from these materials.

It is important that all wire ropes, including escape, extension ladder and turntable ladder cables, be examined for corrosion, fraying and needling. The examination of cables should be carried out in accordance with the *Fire Service Drill Book*.

# Chapter 13
# Knots, bends and hitches

The list of knots, bends and hitches given in this chapter is by no means exhaustive and additional knots may be used, but for normal fire brigade purposes the range described is considered sufficient. Every fireman should not only be familiar with each of these knots, but should know their uses, so that when the occasion arises he will immediately know which is the best knot for the particular job in hand.

The correct method of tying a knot is not difficult to master and, with practice, it should eventually become an ordinary routine in the duties of a fireman. A proportion of the time devoted to practice should be spent with the eyes blindfolded, in order to attain proficiency in the dark. The practice of tying knots with the hands behind the back should not be encouraged as this does not correctly reproduce the conditions when working in smoke or darkness. Mastery in tying such knots as are possible with one hand should also be sought, whilst practice should also be carried out under difficult conditions, such as on ladders or when in the prone position.

The bends, hitches and knots which are given below are those which are in general use by fire brigades, and the terms used in describing bends and hitches are shown in Fig. 13.1. The illustrations have been made as simple as possible so that they may be easily followed. Every knot should be tied with a sufficient

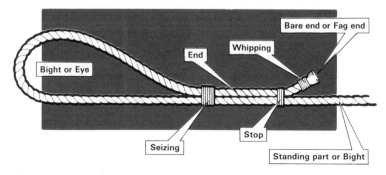

Fig. 13.1 Terms used in describing bends and hitches.

length of running end, but to economise in space, this end is shown in most of the illustrations as shorter than would be the case in practice. An arrow denotes the direction of strain on the line. All knots reduce the strength of a rope in that portion of it where the knot is tied. This reduction varies from 25 to 60 per cent and this fact should be borne in mind when putting a load on a knotted line.

In use a line is always secured to an object, to another line or to part of itself. This is effected by means of a knot or hitch. There are many different knots which are available, each having certain specific uses. The requirements of a good knot are:

(i)   that it shall carry out the function for which it is employed, safely and without slipping;

(ii)  that it shall be easy to make;

(iii) that it shall not damage the line;

(iv)  that it shall be easy to untie.

## 1 Elements of bends and hitches

Most bends and hitches consist of a combination of two or more of the elements shown in Fig. 13.2.

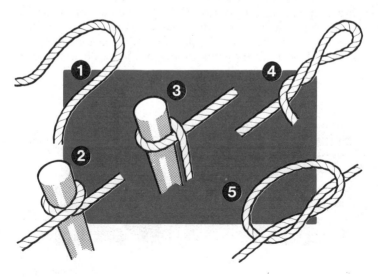

Fig. 13.2 Elements of bends and hitches: (1) a bight; (2) a round turn; (3) a half hitch; (4) a twist; (5) an overhand knot.

## 2 Overhand knot

The overhand knot (Fig. 13.2(5)) is formed by laying the end of
the line over the standing part and bringing it under and up
through the bight. The knot, which is also known as a 'thumb
knot' is mainly used to prevent a line unreeving through a block.
In fire brigade use, the overhand knot is tied in a burst or
damaged length of hose to identify it while it is still laid out.

## 3 Figure-of-eight knot

The figure-of-eight knot (Fig. 13.3) is an alternative to the overhand knot. It is made by laying the end of the line over the
standing part and then bringing the end round underneath the
standing part and down through the bight. This knot is also used
as a stopper to prevent a line unreeving through an eye or block.

Fig. 13.3 Figure-of-eight knot.

## 4 Reef knot

The reef knot is one of the most useful of all knots. It consists
of two overhand knots made consecutively, and is used as a
common tie for bending together two lines of approximately equal
size. Its method of formation can be clearly seen in Fig. 13.4,
but care must be taken to cross the ends opposite ways each time
they are knotted (i.e. right over left and under, then left over
right and under, or vice versa), otherwise the result will be a
'granny' which will slip or jam depending upon whether it is
made with or against the lay of the line. A reef knot lies very

neatly and flat, and the free ends lie parallel, whereas in the granny, the ends are at right angles.

Fig. 13.4 Method of making a reef knot.

## 5 Fisherman's knot

The fisherman's knot (Fig. 13.5) is an alternative to the reef knot, and is used to join lines of equal thickness. A loose overhand knot is made in each end of the lines so that the bight of each knot encloses the other line. Each knot is hauled taut separately

Fig. 13.5 Method of making a fisherman's knot. To complete, each knot is hauled taut separately and then drawn together.

and then the two knots are drawn together. This is sometimes known as a 'sliding double overhand knot'.

The fisherman's knot does not jam so tightly as other knots when subjected to heavy strain, nor when left tied for long periods. It is generally used by fireboat personnel.

## 6 Sheet bends

When lines of unequal thickness have to be joined, a sheet bend should be tied. There are two knots of this type, the single and the double sheet bend. When making a sheet bend, the ends of the two lines are not used simultaneously, as in a reef knot, but a bight is first formed in the end of the thicker line and the thinner line is then passed through it.

The single sheet bend (Fig. 13.6(1)) is formed by passing the end of the thinner line up through the bight in the thicker line,

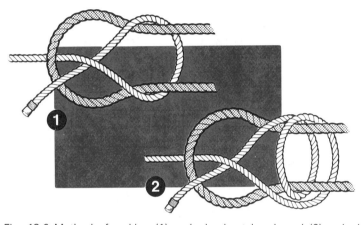

Fig. 13.6 Method of making (1) a single sheet bend, and (2) a double sheet bend.

behind the two parts of the thicker line and under its own standing part, thus forming a locking half hitch round the thicker line. The double sheet bend (Fig. 13.6(2)) is formed in a similar manner, except that the thinner line is given an additional turn round both parts of the thicker line before locking the half hitch.

A double sheet bend should be used when joining wet lines, or lines of man-made fibre whether wet or dry as the extra turn makes the knot more secure.

## 7 Clove hitch

A clove hitch (Fig. 13.7) consists of two half hitches, one of which is reversed. By passing over one another, the parts of the line bind and form a secure hitch which can be easily untied but which will not slip under a steady direct strain. It will, however, slip if subjected to a sideways strain and when this is required a rolling hitch (q.v.) should be used.

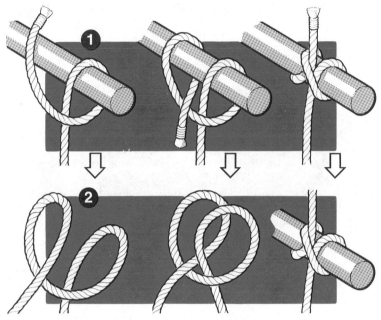

Fig. 13.7 The clove hitch: (1) the clove hitch at the end of a line; (2) the clove hitch on the bight.

Clove hitches can also be made in the middle of a line without using the ends, provided that the hitches can be slipped over the end of the object, such as a spar or a branch. The two half hitches are made at the desired part of the line (Fig. 13.7(2), *left*) by twice passing the line held in the right hand below that held in the left hand, and then bringing the two half hitches together (Fig. 13.7(2), *centre*). The double bight is then slipped over the end of any suitable object and the two hitches are closed together (Fig. 13.7(2), *right*) to form a clove hitch.

The clove hitch is used to make a line fast to a spar, or to secure a line to any object, such as a pump suction. In addition, the clove hitch can be used for hoisting many items of fire brigade equipment, and Fig. 13.8 shows two examples of pieces of equipment being hoisted aloft in a vertical position.

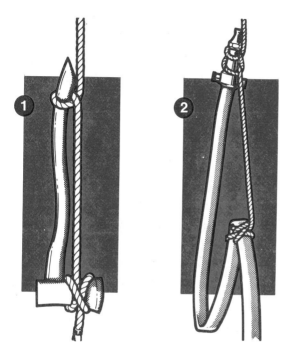

Fig. 13.8 (1) Method of hoisting an axe using a clove hitch on the head and a half hitch on the haft. (2) Method of hoisting a length of hose and a branch using a rolling hitch on the hose and a clove hitch on the branch.

## 8 Rolling hitch

The rolling hitch (Fig. 13.9) is a variant of the clove hitch and is started and finished in the same manner, but an intermediate round turn is made between the two half hitches; this intermediate round turn passes over the standing part. This knot has the advantage that it will not slip in the direction in which the double turn is applied if it is subjected to a sideways pull.

When tying a rolling hitch it must be constructed for the specific strain which it is to resist. Rolling hitches made to take a strain to the left and to the right are shown in Fig. 13.9, left and right respectively. No difficulty should be experienced in tying the knot correctly if it is remembered that the round turn should be made on the same side of the standing part as that on which the strain is to be applied, i.e. if the strain is to the left, then the round turn should be made on the left of the standing part, and vice versa.

The use of a rolling hitch in conjunction with a clove hitch to hoist a length of hose and a branch is shown in Fig. 13.8(2). The rolling hitch should be made on the hose some 3 to 3·5 m from the branch, and adjusted so that when the hose is charged the knot will not restrict the flow. The hose is then allowed to lie in

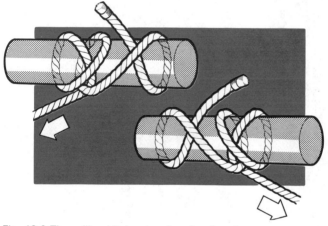

Fig. 13.9 The rolling hitch, showing the direction of strain.

a bight and a clove hitch is made either round the narrowest part of the branch, or round the branch and coupling. When the hose is hoisted, the clove hitch is removed from the branch and the line securing the hose by means of the rolling hitch is then fastened to a suitable firm object in such a way that the hitch lies about 600 to 900 mm below the coping. The line will then take the weight of the charged hose.

## 9 Round turn and two half hitches

A round turn and two half hitches (Fig. 13.10(1)) is formed by making a round turn on a spar or rope, and making two locking half hitches (a clove hitch) on the standing part of the line. The end of the line can then, if desired, be seized to the standing part.

This combination is used to secure a line to a spar, ring or to any round object, or to another line. It has the advantage that whatever stress is applied, the knot will not jam, yet after the weight is removed, it is easy to untie.

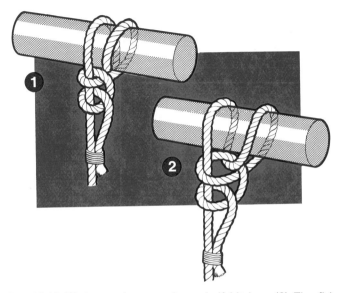

Fig. 13.10 (1) A round turn and two half hitches. (2) The fisherman's bend.

## 10 Fisherman's bend

The fisherman's bend (Fig. 13.10(2)) is an alternative to the round turn and two half hitches, and is made by forming a round turn on the spar or other line to be secured, then making a half hitch round the standing part in such a way that it passes through the round turn. A further half hitch is then made with the end on the standing part. The end should be stopped to the standing part.

This knot, like the round turn and two half hitches, is used to secure a line to a spar or to another line. It is more generally used by fireboat crews to secure a line to a ring bolt.

## 11 Timber hitch

A timber hitch (Fig. 13.11(1)) is made by putting a half hitch on the standing part of a line (after passing the line round the object

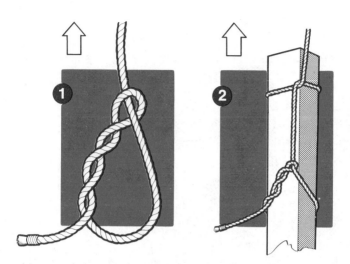

Fig. 13.11 (1) Method of making a timber hitch. (2) Hoisting a spar by means of a timber hitch and a half hitch.

to be secured) and twisting the end back again round its own standing part of the hitch with the lay of the line.

This knot is used to secure a line for hoisting a baulk of timber, a plank or any irregular object. When hoisting a spar, etc. the timber hitch should be used in conjunction with a half hitch (Fig. 13.11(2)) at the upper end of the spar, in order to keep it reasonably upright and to prevent it catching on obstructions. If the spar is tapered, it should be hoisted thick end uppermost, with the timber hitch at the thin end.

## 12 Waterman's hitch

The waterman's hitch (sometimes called the lighterman's hitch) is made by taking several turns round a bollard or bitt, passing the running end over and under the standing part (Fig. 13.12(1)) and then pulling out a bight (a) which is dropped over the bollard, thus forming a figure-of-eight (Fig. 13.12(2)). The line is then hauled taut.

Fireboat crews generally use the waterman's hitch to secure a skiff to the towing bitt of a fireboat. Its virtue is that it can both be made and cast off when under a strain on the standing part.

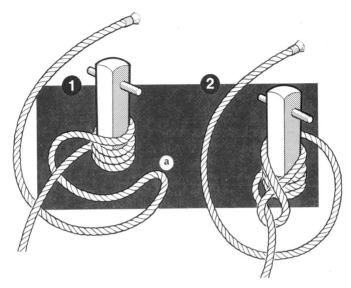

Fig. 13.12 (1) First stage in the method of making a waterman's hitch. (2) The hitch completed.

## 13 Catspaw

A catspaw is formed by throwing back a bight in the line (Fig. 13.13(1)) and then taking each of the two eyes so formed and

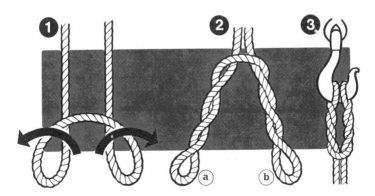

Fig. 13.13 (1) and (2) Method of making a catspaw. (3) Line attached to a hook by means of a catspaw.

twisting them separately outwards from one another, as shown by the arrows. The two eyes (a) and (b) so formed (Fig. 13.13(2)) are then brought together and slipped over the object to which it is desired to secure the line. The catspaw is principally used for attaching a line to a hook (Fig. 13.13(3)).

## 14 Bowline

There are several methods of making a bowline, but the simplest and quickest is as follows: the standing part (a) of the line is held in the left hand and the running end (b) in the right. The running end is then laid across the standing part (Fig.13.14(1)) and a half hitch (c) formed round it by twisting the standing part with the right hand. The knot will then appear as shown in Fig. 13.14(2).

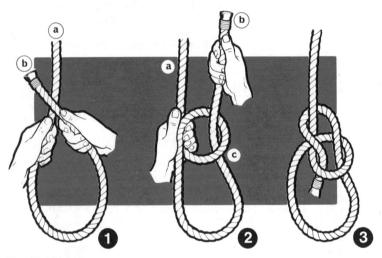

Fig. 13.14 Method of making a bowline.

The half hitch (c) is now secured against the standing part (a) by passing the running end (b) behind the standing part and back down through the half hitch (c)(Fig. 13.14(3)). The knot is then drawn taut.

The bowline forms a non-slipping noose and is useful for lowering or raising purposes, and can also be used to make a temporary eye in lines of all sizes. Another purpose of the bowline is to attach a line round the waist when it is necessary to trail a line, and every fireman should be able to tie a bowline round his own waist with his eyes closed.

## 15 Running bowline

A running bowline (Fig. 13.15) is made by forming a bight (a) in the end of the line by passing the end of the line under the standing part (b) (Fig. 13.15(1)). A bowline is then made with the end at the point (c) on the bight so formed (Fig. 13.15(2)), thus making a running noose.

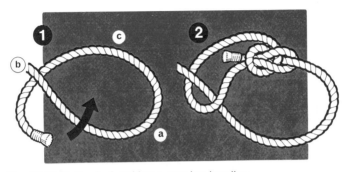

Fig. 13.15 Method of making a running bowline.

A running bowline can be put on a ring, bolt, spar or other object, the ends of which are secured so that the noose cannot be slipped over, by passing the line round the object, leading it under the standing part and back, and then tying a bowline on the loop so formed. A running bowline should *never* be placed round a person's body.

## 16 Bowline on the bight

A bowline on the bight is first formed by making a bight (a) (Fig. 13.16(1)) in the end, or centre, of the line. The bight is then used in the same way as the free end is used when making an ordinary bowline, and a half hitch (b) (Fig. 13.16(2)) is formed on the standing parts (c) of the line. The part of the bight (a) which has been passed through the half hitch is then opened out, and taken in the direction indicated by the arrow (i.e., behind the remainder of the knot) and brought up to the two standing parts (c). The knot is then hauled taut and will appear as shown in Fig. 13.16(3).

145

This knot is used as a sling for rescue purposes. For this the two bights (d) and (e) which are formed (Fig. 13.16(3)) are passed one under the knees and the other under the armpits of the person to be rescued. The knot should be made so that the loop to go round the body is somewhat smaller than the loop for the legs. The respective lengths can be adjusted as required by slackening the knot and pulling the loops to the desired size.

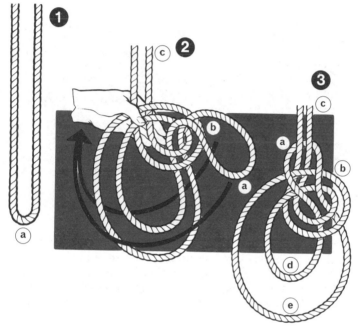

Fig. 13.16 Bowline on the bight.

## 17 Chair knot

The chair knot (Fig. 13.17) is an alternative to the bowline on the bight, and is formed by making two half hitches (a) and (b) (Fig. 13.17(1)) on opposite sides of the line, a portion of each half hitch being then passed through the loop of the other. Part of loop (a) is grasped at (c) and drawn down through loop (b) and part of loop (b) is grasped at (d) and drawn up through loop (a) (Fig. 13.17(2)). These parts are then pulled out to the required length to make the two 'legs' of the knot, and the knot is secured by tying a half hitch round each bight (Fig. 13.17(3)).

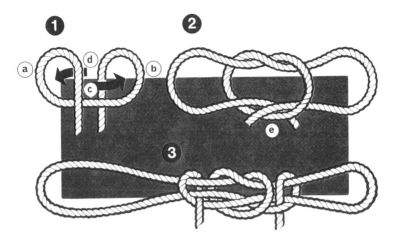

Fig. 13.17 Method of making a chair knot.

There is an alternative method of making a chair knot in which the half hitches are crossed before interlocking them, but this method is not recommended for fire brigade work since it results in a lock at the point (e). The chair knot is used for rescue purposes and has, therefore, to be made with maximum speed. The length of the two bights has invariably to be adjusted, and if the knot is made with a lock at (e) this cannot be done without loosening it. Moreover, a chair knot made by either method cannot slip, since the half hitches round the bight hold it securely once it is drawn tight, and there is therefore no advantage to be gained from the additional lock at (e). The method shown, which enables the knot to be made and adjusted with the minimum of delay, is therefore to be preferred.

A chair knot is used for making a sling for rescue work when a lowering line with legs is not available, or when an injured person has to be lowered on an improvised stretcher. The two loops form the 'hammock' in which the person to be rescued is slung, with one loop under the knees and the other under the armpits. As with the bowline on the bight, the size of the two loops should be adjusted as necessary, bearing in mind the size of the person to be rescued. This is done by pulling more of the ends of the line through the loop before the securing half hitches are hauled taut.

When the length of line permits, both a bowline on the bight and a chair knot are commonly made at the centre of the line. One half of the line is then used for lowering the person and the other part is thrown down to those below to act as a guy line and so keep the person being lowered away from obstructions during the descent.

## 18 Sheepshank

A sheepshank is used to shorten the bight of a line temporarily without cutting it. It is made by gathering up the amount of line by which it is desired to shorten the line as shown in Fig. 13.18(1). Half hitches are then placed around the ends of each bight. The strain on the line will usually prevent the sheepshank from slipping, but if necessary, the loops can be seized to the standing part as shown in Fig. 13.18(2), or alternatively, a piece of wood or a toggle may be inserted in each loop as shown in Fig. 13.18(3).

Fig. 13.18 Method of making a sheepshank.

## 19 Turk's head knot

The Turk's head knot is an ornamental knot which can be made with a light line on a rope or spar for identification, as a handgrip or purely for ornamentation. Typical examples of its use are on bell ropes of appliances, on the grasslines of fireboats and on the shorter leg of a lowering line to denote the standing part. The characteristic formation of this knot can be seen in Fig. 13.19(8), which shows a three-part Turk's head knot. It can be made with any number of parts up to nine, and is then known by the number of parts employed. A three-part Turk's head knot is, however, the one most commonly employed.

The knot is made up as follows:

(1) A half hitch (a) and a turn (b) are first put round the spar or line on which the knot is to be made (Fig. 13.19(1)). Although the knot can be formed by working with both ends of the line, it will be found simpler to learn if the end (d) is kept short and the knot is made up by working with the end (c) only.

(2) The end (c) of the turn (b) is then passed through the bight of the half hitch (a) (Fig. 13.19(2)).

(3) The half hitch (a) is then passed under the bight of the turn (b). The two ends should now lie parallel (Fig. 13.19(3)).

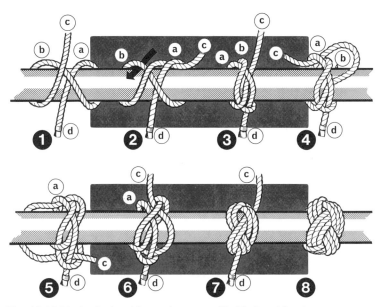

Fig. 13.19 Method of making a three-part Turk's head knot.

(4) The end (c) is then passed through the bight of the half hitch (a), (Fig. 13.19(4)). The knot is now made and all that is necessary to complete it is to follow the lay around. Following round is begun by bringing the end (c) round behind the spar or line and passing it under the same turn as that from which the other end (d) is emerging (Fig. 13.19(5)).

(5) The end (c) is then passed over and under (Fig. 13.19(6) and (7)), following the lay of the knot (i.e. going over and under the same turns as strand (d)), until there are three complete lays of three strands each as shown in Fig. 13.19(8). The knot should then be worked taut and the ends cut off.

# Chapter 14
# General rope work

## 1 Whipping

When a rope is cut, the ends must be secured to prevent them
unlaying, and the simplest method of achieving this is by whipping
with twine. There are many different forms of whipping, some
of which have ornamental finishes.

### a. Natural fibre lines

The most common form of whipping, which is suitable for natural
fibre lines, is carried out as follows: the end (a) of the twine is
placed along the line (Fig. 14.1(1)), and about half a dozen or so
turns of the twine are taken over the line against its lay working

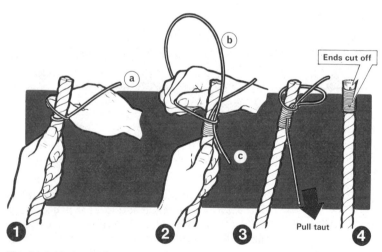

Fig. 14.1 Method of applying a 'common' whipping.

towards the end of the line, each turn being hauled taut. The
twine is then formed into a loop (b) and the end (c) is laid along
the line (Fig. 14.1(2)). The loop is then used to continue the turns

around the line, taking the bight of twine over the end of the line with each turn. When the bight becomes too small to pass over the end of the line, the end (c) is hauled through the turns which have been passed over it until the whole is taut (Fig. 14.1(3)), thus completing the last turn round the line. The protruding ends of the twine (a) and (c) (Fig. 14.1(4)) are then cut off.

An alternative finish, which is necessary if a whipping is on the bight of a line, or if a whipping is to be put on a splice, is to take the last three or four turns loosely over one finger (or a marlinespike) and then to pass the end back through the turns when the finger or marlinespike has been removed. Each turn is worked taut, and the end hauled taut, as above.

## b. Man-made fibre lines

Because of the elasticity of man-made fibre lines, the 'common' whipping is not suitable, and the *palm and needle* whipping (also known as the *sailmaker's* whipping) should be employed. This whipping is the most secure and will not work adrift under any circumstances. The method is as follows: the end of the line is unlaid for about 50 mm and is held in the left hand, pointing upwards, with the middle strand farthest away. A bight (a) about 200 mm long is made in the twine and this is passed over the middle strand only, with the two ends facing forward (Fig. 14.2(1)). Then, with the bight of twine hanging several inches

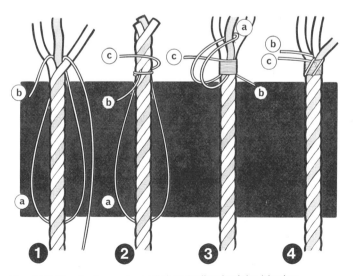

Fig. 14.2 The 'palm and needle' or 'sailmaker's' whipping.

down the back of the line and the ends pointing down in front, the line is relaid again with the right hand. Leaving the short end (b) where it is, the turns of the whipping are made with the long end (c), working towards the end of the line against the lay (Fig. 14.2(2)).

When sufficient turns have been made, the bight of twine (a) is passed up outside the whipping, following the lay of the strand around which it was originally put, and is passed over that strand where the latter comes out at the end of the line (Fig. 14.2(3)). The short end (b) is now hauled taut so as to tighten the bight, and this end is then brought up outside the whipping, again following the lay of the line. The two ends are finally tied in a reef knot in the middle of the line and out of sight (Fig. 14.2(4)).

### c. Whipping of fire brigade lines

B.S. 3367 'Fire Brigade Rescue Lines' specifies that the free end of natural fibre rescue lines shall be securely whipped for a distance of 25 mm with waxed sailmaker's twine. The free end of polyester fibre rescue lines shall be palm and needle whipped for a distance of 25 mm with polyester fibre twine and shall be heat sealed not less than $\frac{1}{4}$ in. (6 mm) away from the whipping: the whipping shall be covered with a tight-fitting rubber or PVC sleeve 25 mm long.

## 2 Seizing

As with whipping, there are many different methods of seizing two lines together. A light seizing (known as a 'flat seizing') for use when the strain on the two parts of the line is equal, but when a stronger seizing is required. It consists of approximately 11 round turns and 10 riding turns laid on top.

A simple flat seizing is shown in Fig. 14.3. The twine is laid doubled alongside the two lines to be seized (Fig. 14.3(1)). Several turns are then taken against the lay round the two lines and also around the end (a) (Fig. 14.3(2), and are hauled taut by pulling on (a). A small piece of wood, or marlinespike, (b) is now inserted alongside the two lines (Fig. 14.3(2), and several more turns are taken with the twine round the lines and the marlinespike in the same direction as before. When sufficient turns have been made, the marlinespike is withdrawn and the end (c) is threaded through the turns towards the centre (Fig. 14.3(3)). The turns are now hauled taut to take up the slack caused by withdrawing the marlinespike (Fig. 14.3(4)). The two ends (a) and (c) are now tied off with a reef knot and the surplus twine is cut off.

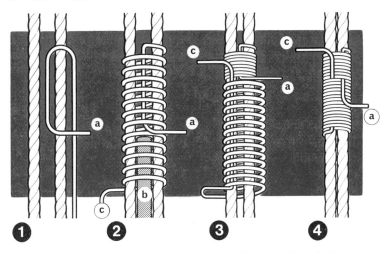

Fig. 14.3 Method of passing a 'flat' seizing. (For the sake of clarity, the two lines are shown apart; they should, obviously, be kept tightly together.)

## 3 Mousing

Mousing consists of securing a piece of cord or wire between the point and the shank of a hook after a chain or a line has been attached to the hook, to prevent unhooking. The method of mousing is shown in Fig. 14.4.

All hooks to which stays are attached, such as on escapes and ladders, should be moused.

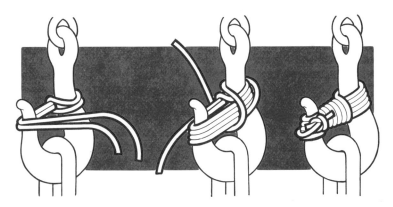

Fig. 14.4 Mousing a hook.

# 4 Splicing

Splicing is a method of joining two lines together, or of making an eye in the end of a line, by interlocking the strands and without the necessity for a knot, which is not only bulky, but also weakens the line.

## a. Types of splice

Of the many different types of splice, the following four are the most commonly used:

(1) Back splice

This is for finishing the end of a rope which is not required to be rove through a block, to prevent it unlaying. It is a more ornate finish than whipping, and many firemen like to back splice their belt lines.

(2) Eye splice

For making a permanent eye in the end of a rope.

(3) Short splice

For joining two ropes.

(4) Long splice

For joining two ropes which are required to pass through a block. A well-made long splice does not increase the diameter of the rope as does a short splice, and should not reduce its strength.

Before starting any kind of splicing, it is advisable to whip the end of each strand. This will prevent the ends becoming unravelled as they are tucked between the strands.

## b. Back splice

A back splice is made by first crowning the line and then tucking each strand back down the line, over and under, against the lay. The line should be whipped at a distance from its end equal to about five times the circumference of the line, and the strands should be unlaid to the whipping (Fig. 14.5(1)).

The crown knot with which the splice is started is made by spreading the strands out in the form of a star with the centre one farthest away from the body; strand (c) is brought to the front to form a loop (Fig. 14.5(1)), strand (a) is placed over (c) and behind (b) (Fig. 14.5(2)), strand (b) is threaded through the loop of (c) Fig. 14.5(3) and all strands are pulled taut until the crown knot is tidy and uniform (Fig. 14.5(4)).

The back splice is continued by cutting the whipping (Fig. 14.5(5)) and then tucking each strand over one strand and under the next, to the left and against the lay of the line as shown in

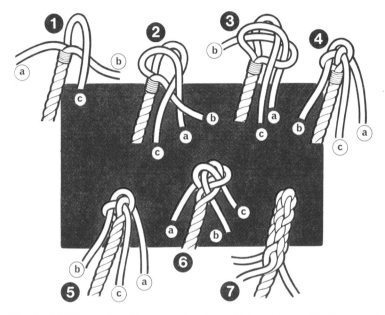

Fig. 14.5 Method of making a back splice: (1) to (4) the splice is started by making a crown knot; (5) to (7) completion of the back splice.

Fig. 14.5(6). After each strand is tucked, it should be pulled taut and this first tuck should be tidied up until each strand is uniform. A marlinespike should be used to open each strand to enable the tuck to be made. The tucking should be repeated twice more (Fig. 14.5(7)). Tucking should always be to the left, using the next strand to the left.

If the splice is to be served, as shown in Fig. 14.6, it should be tapered after the third tuck, as follows: one-third of the yarns are taken out of each strand and the remaining two-thirds tucked in all round as described above (Fig. 14.6(1)); although discarded the thirds should not be cut off until the tapering is completed. The reduced strands are then halved, and one-half of each tucked in, leaving the other half. Finally, all parts should be hauled taut, including the discarded ends, which should now be cut off (Fig. 14.6(2)). The splice can now be whipped to make a neat finish (Fig. 14.6(3)).

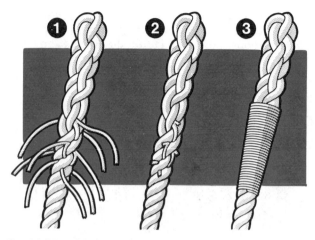

Fig. 14.6 Tapering and serving a back splice.

## c. Eye splice

To make an eye splice, the line should be whipped at a distance from its end equal to five times the circumference of the line, the line should be unlaid to the whipping and each strand should be whipped. The line is then bent to form a loop of the required size and the unlaid strands are laid alongside the place where the splice is to be made with the left and middle strands lying on top of the line (Fig. 14.7(1)).

The middle strand (a) is tucked, from right to left, against the lay, under the nearest strand of the standing part (which has been previously opened with a marlinespike) (Fig. 14.7(2)). Strand (b) is tucked from right to left, against the lay, under the next strand from the standing part (Fig. 14.7(3)). The line should now be turned over, so as to bring the remaining strand (c) on top (Fig. 14.7(4)), and this should be tucked from right to left under the unoccupied strand of the standing part (Fig. 14.7(5)). Care must be taken to retain the lay of the line in the last strand tucked, as this enables it to lie closer. The splice is now started, one tucked strand coming out between each strand of the line, and these three strands should be hauled taut so that the formation of the splice can be more easily followed.

Two more tucks should now be made, each tuck going over one strand of the standing part and under the next, working against the lay (Fig. 14.8(1)). If a neat appearance is required, the eye splice should be tapered, as described for the back splice, and finally served.

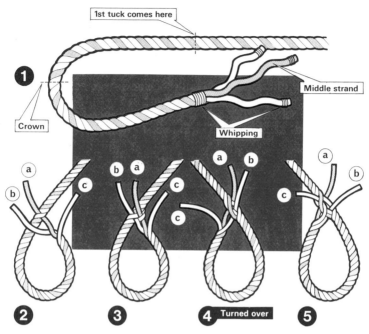

Fig. 14.7 Method of making an eye splice.

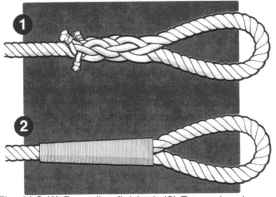

Fig. 14.8 (1) Eye splice finished. (2) Tapered and served.

## d. Short splice

When two lines have to be permanently joined and there is no necessity for the line to be passed through a block, a short splice can be made. The strands of each line are tucked between the strands of the other line against the lay, each strand being taken over the strand on its left, then under the next strand and emerging between this and the subsequent strand. In Fig. 14.9 the ends of the lines are lettered (a) and (b), and their unlaid strands are lettered (c), (d) and (e) and (f), (g) and (h), respectively.

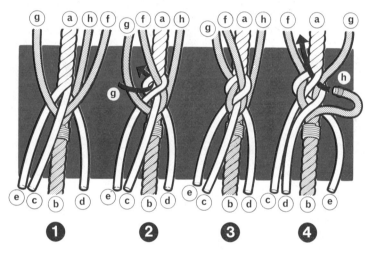

Fig. 14.9 Method of making a short splice. (Certain whippings and stops have been omitted to show the tucking of the strands more clearly.)

Although a short splice can be made simply once its method of construction is understood, difficulty is often experienced in starting the splice owing to the number of loose ends. For this reason each line should be whipped at a distance from its end equal to five times the circumference of the line, and when the strands have been unlaid to the whipping, each strand should be whipped at its end. The whipping has been omitted from (a) in Fig. 14.9.

The two lines are brought together so that one strand of each lies between two strands of the other (Fig. 14.9(1)). Having ensured a close marry, the strands are strongly whipped round the join to prevent them slipping, and ends (c), (d) and (e) are stopped to line (b) (whippings and stops have been omitted in the illustration). The whipping on (a) is now cut, and using a marlines-pike to open the strands, (f) is taken over (c), under (e) and is brought out between (e) and (d) (Fig. 14.9(2); (g) is taken over (e), under (d) and is brought out between (d) and (c) (Fig. 14.9(2 and 3); (h) is taken over (d), under (c) and is brought out between (c) and (e)(Fig. 14.9(4)). Strands (g), (f) and (h) are now stopped to (a), the stop and whipping on (b) are cut and (c), (d) and (e) are tucked in a similar manner.

The splice is now firmly started and all six strands should be hauled taut. Again each strand is tucked over the strand on its left and under the next one, and the operation is repeated a third time (Fig. 14.10). If a tapered end is required, the strands should be reduced for a final tuck, after which the ends should be cut off.

Fig. 14.10 The finish of a short splice.

### e. Long splice

The principle of the long splice differs radically from that of the short splice. One strand from each line is unlaid and one from the other line is given a twist and laid up in its place; the remaining strand from each line remains in the centre, resulting in three pairs of strands spaced equidistantly along the married lines.

To make a long splice, each line is whipped at a distance from its end equal to twelve times the circumference of the line, then the strands are unlaid to the whippings and the ends are whipped. The two lines are married together (Fig. 14.11(1)), as in a short splice. As each strand is unlaid as described above, it is followed up by the strand from the other line which lies on its right in the marriage so that (h) is unlaid and is followed up by (e) (Fig. 14.11(2)), (d) is unlaid and is followed up by (f) (Fig. 14.11(3)), and (c) and (g) remain at the centre (Fig. 14.11(3)). Each strand is unlaid until the end of the strand following it is reduced to four times the circumference of the line. In splicing a 2 in.

(51 mm) line, for example, (h) is unlaid until 200 mm of (e) remains, and (d) is unlaid until 200 mm of (f) remains.

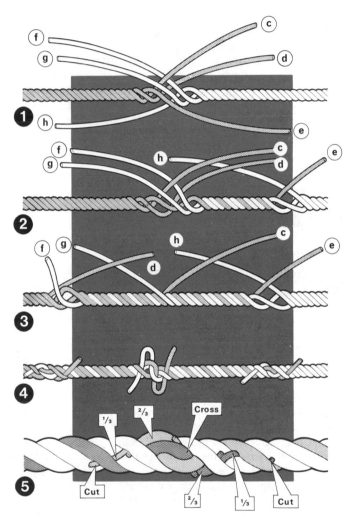

Fig. 14.11 Making a long splice.

One-third of the yarns is now taken out of all strands (not shown in Fig. 14.11(4)), and, though discarded, these yarns should not be cut off until the splice is completed. Each pair of strands is then tied in an overhand knot (left over right for a right-hand-lay rope), and each strand is tucked over one strand and under the next, as for a short splice. Half of the yarns in each strand are now taken out and the remaining yarns tucked once more, to give a gradual taper (Fig. 14.11(5)). The splice is finished off by stretching it, hauling taut all ends (including the discarded yarns) and then cutting them off. A well-made long splice will not increase the diameter of the line, nor will it reduce the strength of the line.

### f. Splicing man-made fibre cordage

Because of their smoothness and elasticity, man-made fibre lines need special care when they are spliced. The strands of the line tend to unlay more readily than the strands of natural fibre lines, and although the normal method of splicing is used, four full tucks should be made instead of three, followed by one-half and one-quarter tucks for a tapered splice. During splicing, care should be taken that:

(i) strands lifted for tucking are not kinked;

(ii) strands are not allowed to run forward, but are pulled back as far as possible;

(iii) the line is kept level the whole time and strands are only lifted high enough for the tuck to take place;

(iv) the line itself is not allowed to kink.

Many turntable ladder rescue lines are now made of plaited polyester fibre and the splicing of such lines is a specialist task. B.S. 3367 specifies that the eye splice in such lines shall be the 'Dickinson' splice (Fig. 14.12). The method of making this splice is described in Appendix D to B.S. 3367.

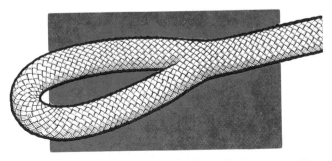

Fig. 14.12 The 'Dickinson' eye splice for plaited polyester fibre lines.

# 5 Strops and slings

Lines are extensively employed in salvage work for moving heavy objects, either by means of a sling or, more rarely, with blocks and tackle, when slings are also required to secure the object to be moved. Care must always be taken when using slings, as their misuse, or their overloading, can be a cause of accidents.

Simple strops, which are merely rings of cordage or wire rope with the end spliced together, are useful to pass round an object for lifting. Such weights should always be slung so that their centre of gravity is as low as possible (Fig. 14.13(1)), and the

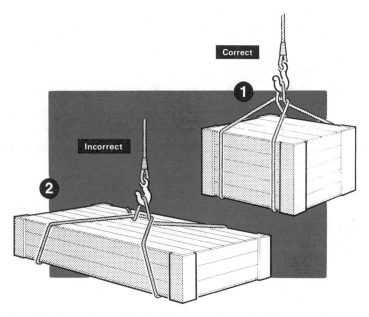

Fig. 14.13 Sketch showing (1) the correct way to sling a case by means of a strop, and (2) the incorrect way.

angles between the four legs of the sling should be kept as small as possible. In Fig. 14.13(2), each leg of the sling bears about $1\frac{1}{2}$ times the weight of the case, whereas in Fig. 14.13(1), the angles between the strop are small and each leg bears about half the weight of the case.

## a. Parbuckle

A parbuckle (Fig. 14.14) is a type of sling which is used to haul up a drum, cask, heavy spar or similar object. When using a parbuckle, the two parts of the line must be paid out or hauled in equally, in order to prevent the cask or other object from slipping out of the sling.

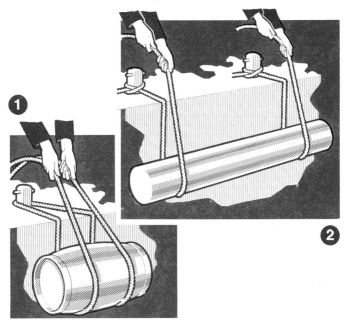

Fig. 14.14 (1) Hoisting a cask by parbuckling. (2) Use of a parbuckle to lower a baulk of timber.

## b. Slinging a cask

(1) Horizontally

To sling a cask on its side (Fig. 14.15(1), a running bowline (a) is made at the end of the line, and the loop so formed is placed over one end of the cask and is hauled taut. The end of the line is then taken around the other end of the cask and hitched to its own part by a clove hitch (b). A hook or another line can then be attached at (c) to the sling. When slinging a cask on its side, the bung should be kept uppermost.

(2) Upright

To sling a cask in an upright position (Fig. 14.15(2)), the line is passed under the cask and an overhand knot is made with the ends on top of it; the knot is then opened out and the two halves are slid down the sides to a quarter of the way down the cask. The whole is hauled taut and the ends are tied with a reef knot at the top.

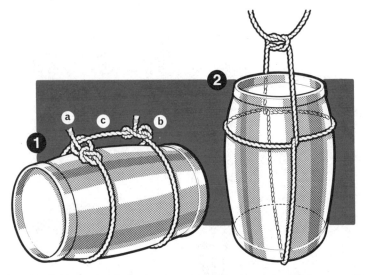

Fig. 14.15 Methods of slinging a cask: (1) horizontally; (2) in an upright position.

# 6 Blocks and tackle

A *purchase* is a mechanical device by means of which an applied pull or force is increased; it may be a system of levers, a system of revolving drums or wheels geared to one another, or a combination of blocks and pulleys rove with rope or chain. A *tackle* is a purchase consisting of a rope rove through two or more blocks in such a way that any pull applied to its hauling part is increased by an amount depending on the number of sheaves in the blocks and the manner in which the rope is rove through them.

## a. Blocks

A block is a portable pulley, made of wood, metal or wood and metal. The main parts of a block (Fig. 14.16) are the *shell* or body, the *sheave* or wheel over which the rope rungs, the *pin* on which the sheave turns, the *bush* or bearing between the sheave and the pin, and the eye, hook, strop or other fitting by which the block is secured in the required position.

The top of the block where the eye or hook is fitted is called the *crown,* the bottom of the block is the *tail,* the sides of the shell are the *cheeks,* the groove made in the cheeks of some blocks to take the strop is called the *score,* the opening between the sheave and the shell through which the rope passes is the *swallow,* and the eye sometimes fitted to the tail is the *becket.*

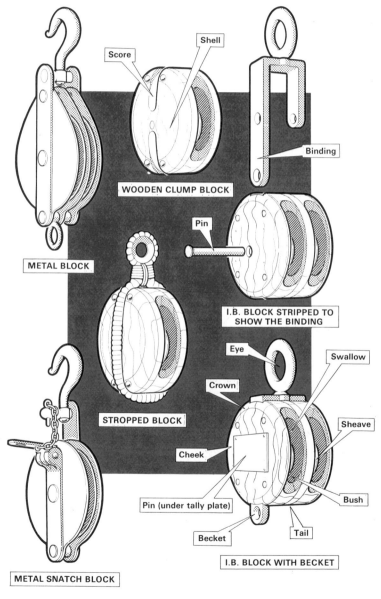

Fig. 14.16 Various types of block, and the names of the parts of a block.

Wooden blocks are classified by their size, which is their length from crown to tail measured round the shell; an ordinary wooden block will take a rope one-third of its size, so that a 150 mm block, for example, would be required to take a 50 mm rope. Metal blocks are classified by the size of rope for which each is designed, and the size is marked on a plate fixed to one cheek. Blocks may have more than one sheave; a single block has one sheave; a double block, two; a tripe block, three, and so on.

Modern wooden blocks, known as *internal-bound (IB) blocks,* have a shell partly of wood and partly of metal. *Common blocks,* which are an old-fashioned type of block, are held in position by a strop passed round the shell and seized into a thimble-eye at the crown; the strop thus strengthens the shell and the block. The *clump block* can be of wood or metal and has an exceptionally large swallow. *Snatch blocks* are single blocks, either of metal or internally-bound, in which part of the shell is hinged to allow a bight of rope to be inserted into the swallow from one side. Every block, except a stopped block, has a fitting at its crown by which to secure it when required.

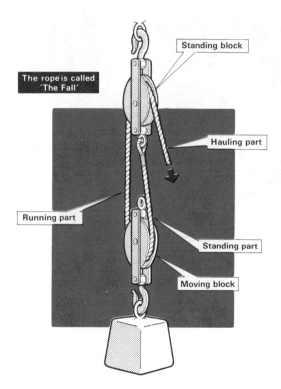

Fig. 14.17 Parts of a tackle.

## b. Tackle

The blocks of a tackle are known as the *standing block* and the *moving block* (Fig. 14.17); the rope which is rove through the blocks is called the *fall,* and has its *standing, running* and *hauling* parts.

### (1) Mechanical advantage and velocity ratio

The amount by which the pull in the hauling part is multiplied by the tackle is known as the *mechanical advantage* (MA) and, disregarding friction, this is equal to the number of parts of the fall at the moving block. In Fig. 14.18(1), there are two parts at the moving block and therefore the mechanical advantage is 2; in

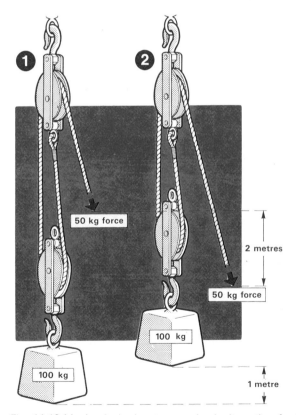

Fig. 14.18 Mechanical advantage and velocity ratio of a tackle.

other words, it only requires a force of 50 kg (= 490 newtons) on the hauling part to raise a weight of 100 kg.

Mechanical advantage, however, is only gained at the expense of speed of working, and it will be seen in Fig. 14.18(2), that for any two metres of movement of the hauling part, the weight will only be raised one metre. The ratio between the distance moved by the hauling part and that moved by the moving block is known as the *velocity ratio,* and is always equal to the number of parts of the fall at the moving block.

When a tackle is being used, however, considerable friction is set up, both in the bearings of the blocks and within the fall as it bends round the sheaves. This friction accounts for the difference between the mechanical advantage and the velocity ratio of the tackle. For example, in a tackle where the velocity ratio is 3, the mechanical advantage may only be about 2·3.

## (2) Reeving to advantage

The number of parts at the moving block, and therefore the mechanical advantage, is always greater when the hauling part comes away from the moving block, and a tackle in such circumstances is said to be *rove to advantage* (Fig. 14.19(1)), whereas when the hauling part comes away from the standing block (Fig. 14.19(2)), the tackle is said to be *rove to disadvantage.*

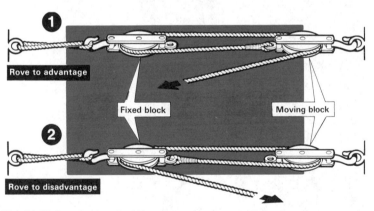

Fig. 14.19 Reeving tackle (1) to advantage, and (2) to disadvantage.

## c. Use of tackle

The simplest method of raising a weight by means of a block and tackle is to reeve the line through a single block, attach one end of the line to the weight, and haul on the other. This is the single whip of the line to the weight, and haul on the other. This is the

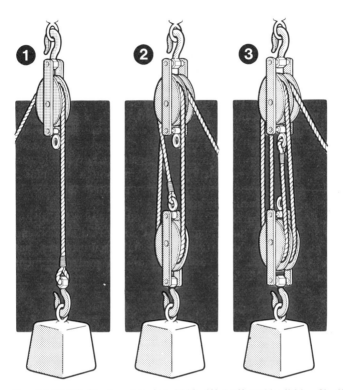

Fig. 14.20 (1) Single whip (no MA). (2) Luff tackle (MA = 3). (3) Two-fold purchase or double luff tackle (MA = 4).

single whip (Fig. 14.20(1)) where there is no mechanical advantage and the velocity ratio is 1 : 1. When the weight is too heavy to be lifted by this means, the introduction of additional blocks will increase the mechanical advantage. In Fig. 14.20(2 and 3) are shown examples of a luff tackle, where the mechanical advantage is three times, and a two-fold purchase or double luff tackle, where the mechanical advantage is four times, in both cases disregarding friction.

It will be seen that the manner in which a tackle is rove is of practical importance, and if an alternative is possible, the position of maximum advantage should always be employed. The manner in which a tackle is rove is, however, conditioned by the lead of the hauling part of the fall (i.e. by whether the object to be moved is being drawn *towards* the person hauling, in which case the fall leads from the moving block, or *away* from him, in which case it leads from the standing block, although this position is rove to disadvantage.

Before a tackle is rove, the blocks should be examined to ensure that they are well lubricated and free from dirt or grit. The strops, blocks and falls must be in good condition, the pins made fast and the standing end of the fall secure. The fall must, of course, always be free from kinks. When hauling, after the fall is taut, the load should be hauled steadily and not jerked. The fall should always lie in a straight line with the sheaves, thus avoiding any damage to the fall, or any strain where the tackle is attached. A haul in a straight line with the sheave will ensure the smooth running of the falls. All hooks or shackles of tackles should be moused to prevent them from becoming unshipped. When lowering, the line should never be allowed to run though the hands, but should always be paid out hand over hand, or a turn should be taken round some secure object.

When setting up a purchase, a pole should be erected horizontally about 1·8 m from the ground, and be supported at each end on sheer legs. This should suffice for normal circumstances, but in each individual case, the varying conditions and equipment available will have to be considered.

# Glossary of terms relating to ropes and cordage

**Angle of lay.** The angle at which the strands lie in relation to the axis of the rope.

**Belay.** To make a line fast. This is usually applied to running lines.

**Bend.** To fasten a line to another line or to an object.

**Bight.** The middle part of a length of line. The term also refers to a loop of a line, and to 'make a bight' is to form a loop.

**Breaking load.** The load which, when applied to a rope, line, twine, cord, strand or yarn, will cause complete rupture.

**Cable or cable-laid.** The ultimate product when three or more ropes are twisted to form a helix round the central axis, where the ropes forming the final strand are S-lay and the finished cable Z-lay, or vice versa.

**Crowning.** A method of finishing off the end of a line, when extra thickness at the end is not inconvenient, by unlaying the strands and making a crown knot (see Fig. 14.5), such as at the start of a back splice.

**End.** The short length at either end of a line, which may be formed into an eye, or used for making a bend or hitch with which to secure it. The end of a line is also that length of rope left over after making such an eye, bend or hitch.

**Factor of safety.** The figure by which the breaking strength of new rope is divisible to determine its safe working load.

**Hawser-laid.** Rope which is made from three strands laid up in the opposite direction to the lay of the strand.

**Hawser.** A hawser-laid rope. The term is generally used, particularly at sea, to indicate large ropes of 150 mm circumference and over. The true definition is 'a rope consisting of three strands laid up in the opposite direction to the strands'. As strands are commonly laid up left-handed, most hawsers are laid right-handed.

**Hitch.** A simple fastening of a line to some object by passing the line round the object and crossing one part over the other.

**Laid.** A descriptive term to indicate the style of making up. Hawser-laid indicates a three-strand rope; shroud-laid indicates a four-strand rope and cable-laid a nine or more strand rope.

**Lay.** The pitch of one complete turn of a strand measured in a straight line parallel to the axis of the rope.

**Line.** Cordage cut to a specified length for a particular purpose, i.e., lowering line, rescue line, belt line. The term is derived from the use of ropes at sea, and is commonly used to distinguish between the manufacturer's product in bulk (i.e. 219 metres of 50 mm manila rope, etc.), and the lengths which are cut from it.

**Mousing.** A piece of cord or light line tied across a hook (see Fig. 14.4) to prevent the object secured to the hook from unhooking.

**Parcelling.** The wrapping of a line, or part of a line, usually with strips of canvas, to prevent chafing (see 'serving').

**Pay out.** To ease out or to slacken a line.

**Reeve.** To thread a line through a block.

**Rope.** The ultimate product when three or more strands are laid together to form a helix round a central axis. The term *rope* should not be used when the ultimate product has a circumference of less than 12·5 mm or a diameter of less than 4 mm, in this case cord or thread (q.v.) would be used.

**Running end.** The free end of a line.

**Running part.** The moving part of a line which is loose and is used to hoist or to lower.

**Seizing.** A seizing is used to fasten together two ropes or cables, or two parts of the same rope or cable, to prevent them moving in relation to each other.

**Serving.** The protection of a line against chafing by winding yarn on it against the lay (see Fig. 14.6). A line is always served after it has been parcelled.

**Shroud-laid.** A four-strand rope with the strands of helical formation.

**Splicing.** A method of joining the ends of two ropes together, or of making an eye in the end of a rope, by unlaying the strands for a short distance, and then interlocking the strands of the two parts into one another. A long splice (see Fig. 14.11) is used to join two ropes which are required to be rove through a pulley block. A short splice (see Fig. 14.9) is simpler, but as the splice increases the size of the ropes, it cannot be rove through a block.

**Standing part.** The part of the bight of a line which is nearest the eye, bend or hitch, in contrast to the end.

**Stopping.** A light fastening for temporarily holding in place a line or any object. It is not meant to bear any strain other than that required to keep the line or other object in place.

**Strand.** The product obtained by twisting together two or more yarns.

**Tensile strenth.** The load at the time of rupture divided by the original cross-sectional area of the rope, strand, twine or line being tested.

**Thread.** A slender cord made from two or more yarns or filaments twisted together.

**Twine.** A number of yarns twisted or laid to produce a balanced twisted structure of continuous length.

**Whipping.** The binding around the end of a line to prevent the strands from unlaying.

**Worming.** Laying a light line within the grooves between strands of a line in order to give a smooth surface before parcelling.

**Yarn.** The product of spinning together fibres of regular or irregular staple length so that they are bound together by twist to form a continuous length.

# Part 4
# Small gear and miscellaneous equipment

Small gear is a term commonly used in the fire service when referring to the miscellany of tools and items of equipment which cannot be classified under other main headings, but which are nevertheless essential to the fireman if he is to tackle effectively the wide variety of tasks which he is called upon to perform. This Part deals with the various items of small gear and miscellaneous equipment which are to be found on fire appliances.

Although at first glance the display of small gear carried may present a rather heterogeneous appearance, it is in fact a most carefully selected assortment of equipment, based upon practical experience over many years and designed to assist the fireman to maintain a jealously-guarded reputation that he can always do something useful in an emergency which involved the safety of lives and property. Included are items of tools and equipment to facilitate such tasks as breaking into premises by forcing doors and locks; cutting through walls, floors and roofs for access or ventilation purposes; cutting out defective hearths; the rescue of persons and animals trapped in unusual circumstances; the removal of heavy objects such as debris, timber or machinery which are hindering operations; turning over and salvage operations, and many more.

# Chapter 15
# General purpose tools and equipment

A considerable number of well-known conventional tools of various kinds are commonly used by fire brigades and, since they are virtually the same as those used in other work, it has not been thought necessary to give them more than a brief mention here. Where conventional tools form part of a special kit, they are given in detail as necessary. Tools under this general-purpose heading include spades, pickaxes, mattocks, large axes, sledgehammers, steel crowbars and wedges; carpenters' tools such as hammers, wood saws and chisels of various kinds and sizes, ratchet braces and bits, screwdrivers, etc.; fitters' tools such as spanners and wrenches, hacksaws, cold chisels, breast drills, pliers and wire cutters, etc.

## 1 General

### a. Specifications

The Joint Committee on Design and Development of Fire Appliances and Equipment of the Central Fire Brigades Advisory Council issues for the guidance of fire authorities and manufacturers, specifications which include suggested equipment to be carried on the various appliances, and also a general guide as to where the various items of equipment might be suitably accommodated.

Whilst these JCDD specifications purport to be no more than a general guide as to what equipment might be carried, there is nevertheless some measure of uniformity throughout the country in the type of small gear and specialised equipment used by fire brigades, although there is quite considerable variation in the detail of various pieces of equipment adopted and used by individual brigades.

### b. Stowage

Because of variations in the design of fire appliances manufactured for different fire authorities, it is not practicable nationally to adopt a standard stowage plan for small gear and miscellaneous equipment. Each brigade normally has a standard stowage plan for each type of fire appliance, as it is essential for each member of a crew to know, especially when working in the dark, exactly where he can find each item of equipment carried on the appliance.

The preparation of appliance equipment stowage plans receives very careful consideration, and the provision of suitable hooks, slots, brackets and other fittings ensures that there is only one place for each piece of equipment, that all equipment is readily visible and accessible and that it will not accidentally become displaced.

### c. Standard tests and maintenance

The small gear and miscellaneous equipment referred to in this chapter requires in general little maintenance other than periodic inspection, cleaning and perhaps sharpening, but where standard tests apply, they appear in the *Fire Service Drill Book*. Where special maintenance is required, it is mentioned under the heading of the item of equipment involved.

### d. Danger of electrical contact

Every fireman should be aware of the dangers involved in making contact, either directly or indirectly, with *live* electrical wiring or equipment. Some of the tools used by fire brigades have insulated handles (e.g. pliers and cutters and some firemen's axes), but it is unsafe to assume that such tools afford adequate protection to enable the user to make safe contact with live electrical installations, especially when water or even dampness is present. This aspect is covered in detail in the *Manual, Part 6B: Chapter 3, 'Electricity and the Fire Service'*, which emphasises the risk involved even when wearing rubber gloves.

## 2 The fireman's axe

The fireman's axe is normally a part of every fireman's personal gear, together with his belt and axe-pouch, but it is also carried in hook belts used with hook and turntable ladders. Firemen's axes are also carried on some fire appliances as spares or as an alternative to issue as personal equipment. There are two types in general use, both of which are covered by separate British Standards, one having a wooden handle and the other an insulated steel handle. Local preference normally decides which of the two types is used by individual brigades.

### a. Fireman's axe with wooden handle

This type of axe (Fig. 15.1(1)) is covered by B.S. 2957 which relates to the dimensions, quality and performance of wooden-handled axes intended for fire brigade use.

Specially hardened steel, polished and treated with clear lacquer or other such finish as may be required by the purchaser, is used for the axe head. The handle is made from well-seasoned best straight-grained ash with a natural sanded finish. The overall length is about 375 mm and the axe weighs between 900 to 1130 g. The handle is fitted right through the head, and two countersunk head rivets secure the head straps to the handle.

The wooden-handled axe provides no protection to the user against injury by electric shock other than the limited insulation properties of the wooden handle.

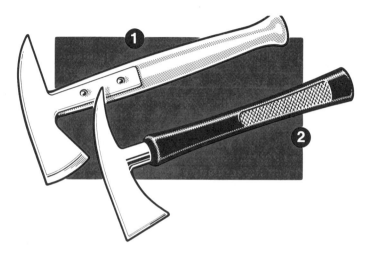

Fig. 15.1 The fireman's axe. (1) with wooden handle; (2) with insulated steel handle.

### b. Fireman's axe with insulated steel handle

British Standard 3054 was prepared with the object of ensuring that this type of axe (Fig. 15.1(2)) is suited to fire brigade conditions and that it may be interchangeable with the ash-handled axe in the normal pouch.

Emphasis is laid in the British Standard on the fact that the insulated-handled axe is not intended as a piece of special equipment which will permit personnel deliberately to operate on live electrical circuits, but that it should be regarded as a tool that could give an added degree of safety in circumstances where a live electrical circuit may be accidentally touched. The fact that the handle of the axe is covered with an insulant is not in itself a guarantee that the user is safe from electric shock, and therefore additional safeguards must be observed when work is carried out on electrical equipment, particularly in view of the fact that the axe may often be used in wet conditions.

As well as relating to the dimensions, quality, finish and performance of axes with rubber-insulated handles, the British Standard lays down test requirements to be met during production as well as final physical and electrical tests on the finished article. It also points out that some manufacturers treat the complete tool with lacquer, and regards this as permissible provided a non-conducting clear lacquer is used and that the tool is still capable of passing the test requirements.

The axe head complete with tang is made from specially hardened steel and the handle is made of black rubber, which is moulded to the steel tang. The dimensions and weight are about the same as for the ash-handled axe. Each axe that has passed the electrical test laid down in the British Standard should have a 25 mm wide blue rubber band secured to the insulated handle between the chequered grip and the head, and this band should bear the date of test and the caption 'Passed B.S. 3054 tests'. An appendix to the British Standard deals with recommendations for the storage, care, inspection and periodic re-testing of firemen's axes with rubber insulated handles.

The insulation should not be unnecessarily exposed to heat or allowed to come into contact with oil, grease, turpentine, motor spirit or acid. When the insulation becomes soiled, it should be thoroughly washed with soap and water, and dried. If it should become contaminated with tar or paint, it can be wiped clean with a suitable solvent which is not injurious to rubber, and then immediately washed and treated as above. Petrol or paraffin should not be used for removing such compounds.

Firemen's axes with rubber insulated handles should be examined at the times stated and in accordance with the *Fire Service Drill Book*.

### c. Fireman's axe pouch

Pouches constructed to a number of different designs, including those with a complete flap and a cut-away flap, were examined

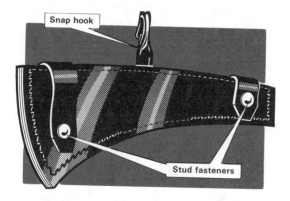

Fig. 15.2 Firemen's leather axe pouch to the new specification issued by the Joint Committee on Uniform and Personal Equipment of the CFBAC.

by the Joint Committee on Uniform and Personal Equipment of the Central Fire Brigades Advisory Council, in an attempt to find a pouch which did not have a tendency for the axe to ride up out of the pouch, which was as light in weight and as compact as possible and which allowed the axe to be withdrawn freely. All the designs examined could be faulted on some point and the Committee decided that the two-strap design, which could only be criticised on the grounds of having two fasteners, was the most acceptable.

A new specification was issued by the Joint Committee to replace the old one. The pouch (Fig. 15.2) to which the new specification applies, is allowed a choice in the type of fastening and in the use of either chrome or vegetable-tanned leather. Chrome leather affords greater resistance to the effects of heat and water, but is likely to prove more difficult to polish to a high gloss. In order to improve the hang of the axe, the specification provides for the snap-hook to be sited near the top of the pouch.

## 3 The ceiling hook

The ceiling hook (Fig. 15.3) consists of a pole from 2 to 2·4 m long having at the top a steel point with a spur at right angles, the point and spur each being about 100 mm long.

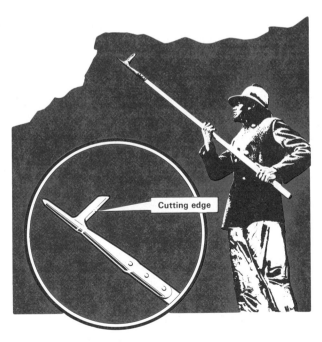

Cutting edge

Fig. 15.3 Ceiling hook.

This tool is of interest as being one of the few items of small gear which were primarily developed for fire brigade use. Its relationship to a boat-hook is, of course, obvious, but in its present form, it is exclusively a fire brigade tool. The ceiling hook is now commonly used to pierce a ceiling to allow water to escape and thus prevent the possible collapse of the ceiling itself due to the weight of water. The spur is used for pulling down ceilings which have partially fallen and are in a dangerous condition. The hook is driven up through the ceiling and the spur is twisted until a grip is obtained on any projecting laths. A sharp pull will then bring down a portion of the laths and plaster; the operation is then repeated until the ceiling is considered safe. The same procedure may also be followed for pulling down lath and plaster walls.

The ceiling hook is a general purpose tool which is frequently used during turning-over and pulling-down operations and for any job which calls for a long reach with a rigid piece of equipment, as, for exampe, the operation of the fireman's switch, usually located about 2·4 m above ground level, on high-voltage neon lighting installations.

## 4 Chimney rods

A set of chimney rods will be found on most first-line fire appliances and, as explained in the *Manual, Book II, Part 1, Chapter 5, 'Dealing with various types of fires'*, are used in conjunction with hose reel or stirrup pump hose when dealing with chimney fires.

Chimney rods consist of a series of stout but flexible malacca canes with screw joints at each end, similar to those used by chimney sweeps. Attached to the head of the first rod is a chimney nozzle (see page 62) which is designed so that it will not catch against the rough interior of a chimney. After the first section, with nozzle and tubing attached, has been pushed up the chimney, additional rods are connected until the nozzle can be raised to the required height.

## 5 Hearth kit

As the name implies, a hearth kit is used for opening up or removing hearths and fireplaces to enable an otherwise inaccessible fire to be revealed and extinguished (see the *Manual, Book II, Part 1, Chapter 5, 'Dealing with various types of fires'*.

A hearth kit is carried on most first line appliances and although the kits used in different brigades may vary to a certain extent in detail, the one illustrated in Fig. 15.4 may be regarded as typical.

It consists of the following tools:

Bricklayer's bolster.
Two cold chisels.
Club hammer.
Insulated pliers.
Floorboard saw.
Hacksaw.
Spare hacksaw blades.
Screwdriver.

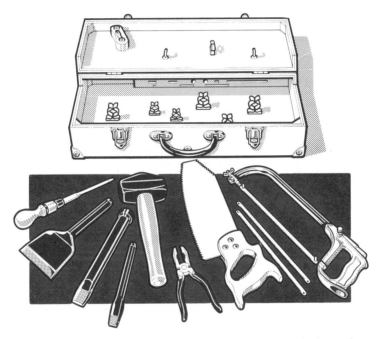

Fig. 15.4 A hearth kit, showing the type of box in which the tools are generally stowed.

## 6 Canvas buckets

Collapsible canvas buckets of capacities varying from 9—18 litres are carried for general purpose usage on many fire appliances. They can be folded or rolled, and occupy only a small amount of locker space. Before being stowed, canvas buckets should be thoroughly dried to prevent the formation of mildew; in short, their care and maintenance should generally be the same as for canvas hose.

## 7 Crowbars

Crowbars of various types form an essential part of the equipment of fire appliances. The most common type consists of a steel bar about 1 metre in length, either one or both ends of which are shaped at an angle to provide leverage. One end is usually claw-shaped for use when levering out nails, screws and other fittings, whilst the other end is chisel-shaped. Crowbars are used to provide the necessary leverage to facilitate the forcing of doors and windows and the removal of fittings and objects which may be found to impede fire fighting or rescue operations.

## 8 The steel-shod lever

The steel-shod lever (Fig. 15.5) consists of a straight wooden shaft, usually of seasoned ash, about 50 mm diameter, increasing

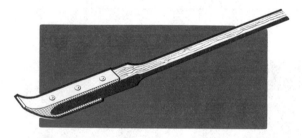

Fig. 15.5 Steel-shod wooden lever.

to about 75 mm in square section at one end, to which is riveted a heavy iron shoe with a slightly upturned chisel-shaped tip. The steel-shod lever is used for breaking open steel doors and other obstructions, the tip being inserted under the door and leverage exerted. It is also used for lifting blocks of stone or concrete, heavy baulks of timber and other material when turning over.

## 9 Doorbreakers

Doorbreakers are sometimes used by fire brigades and several different types of proprietary tool are obtainable. They all work by the application in one way or another of the lever principle, and the example illustrated in Fig. 15.6 consists of a steel lever to which is attached, by means of a pivot, a telescopic strut which terminates in a pivoted claw plate. Application of upward pressure to the lever handle exerts sufficient force on the claw plate either to break in a panel or to force a door open.

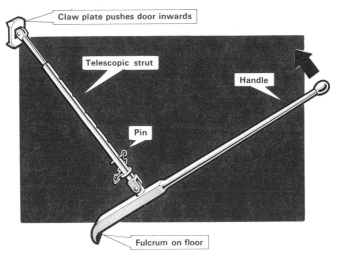

Fig. 15.6 One type of doorbreaker.

## 10 Padlock remover

Some form of special lever or other tool, often of local design and construction, is frequently to be found amongst the equipment

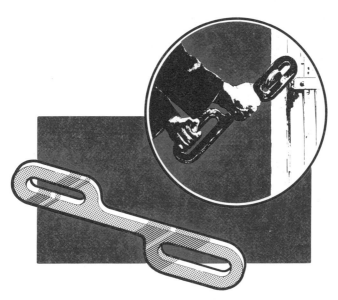

Fig. 15.7 A padlock remover, showing method of use.

on fire appliances to facilitate the rapid removal of padlocks. One example of this type of tool is illustrated in Fig. 15.7 the padlock being inserted in one of the two openings in the tool whilst the other end is used to give sufficient leverage to force either the lock or hasp.

When no special tools are available, many padlocks can easily be forced by wedging the hasp against the door with the hinge downwards and giving the body of the lock a sharp blow with a hammer, axe or other suitable tool (see also the *Manual, Book II, Part 2, Chapter 6, 'Methods of entry'*.

## 11 Persuader

Persuader is a term commonly used in the fire service to describe a tool consisting of a cigar-shaped cold chisel to which a steel handle is secured (Fig. 15.8), and it is normally used for forcing

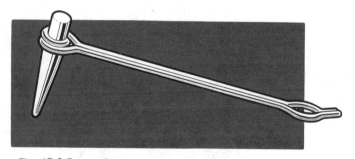

Fig. 15.8 Persuader.

padlocks which cannot be dealt with by the use of padlock removers, crowbars or other available tools.

The point of the chisel is blunt since the function of the tool is not to cut but to break a padlock by the expanding effect of the tapered chisel being forced into the loop of the hasp by blows from a heavy hammer.

## 12 Spreaders

Spreaders, or expanding tools, of various kinds are used by fire brigades for forcing apart iron bars, such as railings, usually to facilitate the release of trapped persons or animals. Fig. 15.9 illustrates one type of railing spreader in current use which consists of a nut threaded internally to receive two 'V'-shaped lugs with threaded stems. A handle in the form of a tommy bar fits into a hole bored through the sides of the nut. The 'V'-shaped lugs are placed against the bars to be moved, and when the nut is rotated by means of the tommy bar, the lugs are forced outwards, thus forcing the bars apart (Plate 14).

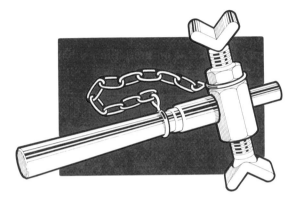

Fig. 15.9 A railing spreader.

## 13 Bending bars

Bending bars, or wring-irons as they are sometimes called, are usually carried on emergency tenders and sometimes on other appliances. They are used for bending metal rods, bars or sheeting which impede rescue or fire-fighting operations.

Many different types and sizes of bending bar are used, but they all apply the principle of leverage in one way or another to produce the desired results. Fig. 15.10 illustrates one common

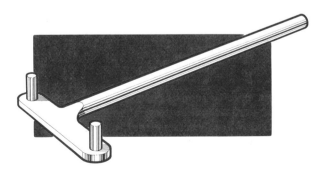

Fig. 15.10 A bending bar.

type of bending bar which consists of a solid steel handle about 1·2 m in length terminating in a plate which carries two solid lugs both about 50 mm long. The lugs are placed one on each side of the object to be bent and leverage is applied by means of the handle so that one lug holds the object secure while the other bends it.

## 14 Cutters

Cutters of various types are carried on most fire appliances and are used for cutting metal bolts and padlock hasps to facilitate entry into warehouses and other premises which are protected by heavily bolted doors. They are also used in circumstances where metal obstacles impede fire fighting or rescue operations.

Fig. 15.11 illustrates an example of one type of general purpose cutter used by fire brigades. The jaws are operated on a double

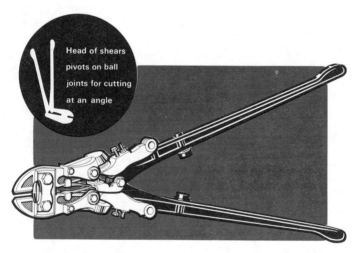

Head of shears pivots on ball joints for cutting at an angle

Fig. 15.11 Typical pair of shears with pivoted head for cutting at an angle.

fulcrum and sometimes have semi-circular slots in each blade to enable the tool to be used as bolt cutters. The handles are pivoted on ball joints so that when necessary the head can be used at right angles to the handles.

Various types of purpose-made tool are used for cutting bolts and padlock hasps, a typical example of one being illustrated in Fig. 15.12. With this type of bolt cutter, the action of the jaws is controlled by a threaded attachment which is hand-operated by the turning of a knob.

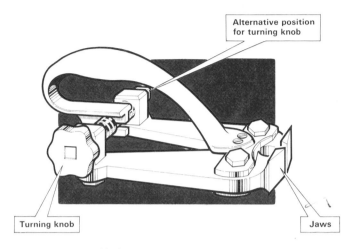

Fig. 15.12 Typical bolt cutter.

## 15 Quick-release knives

A special type of knife, known as a quick-release knife (Fig. 15.13) is sometimes carried on appliances for use in emergencies to facilitate the speedy release of persons trapped by harness, belts or straps, such as, for example, persons trapped in belted machinery.

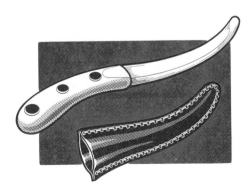

Fig. 15.13 A quick-release knife.

The cutting edge of the slightly curved blade should be kept very sharp, whereas the outer edge and tip are thick with a smooth rounded finish. This design enables the knife to be used speedily without fear of cutting the casualty, by inserting it inside the belt or strap with the blunt edge against the person's body.

## 16 Cold set

A cold set is a blacksmith's tool used for cutting metal bars without first heating them, and is carried on some emergency tenders. It consists of a short specially hardened form of cold chisel secured in a metal handle which is held by one man whilst another strikes the chisel head with a sledgehammer.

## 17 Rural implements

Special tools likely to be used in connection with rural fire fighting, such as beaters, stack drags or billhooks, are described and illustrated in the *Manual, Part 6B: Chapter 1, 'Fires in rural areas'.*

## 18 Lifting equipment

A considerable variety of different types of lifting equipment is used by fire brigades and includes hydraulic jacks of various kinds and sizes, air lifting bags, portable winches, chain blocks and tackle, sheer legs, etc. Although certain items of lifting equipment are sometimes carried on first line appliances which may be expected to be the first attendance at road accidents, or alternatively be kept available at fire stations, lifting equipment is normally associated with emergency tenders and breakdown lorries.

## 19 Electric power tools

Electrically-operated hand tools of various kinds, such as drills and saws, are used by many fire brigades, but since these items are usually carried on emergency tenders, they are dealt with in the *Manual, Book 5, Chapter 14,* which deals with special appliances and their equipment.

## 20 Rubber gloves

Most fire-fighting appliances carry special rubber gloves for use when it is essential for a fireman to work in dangerous proximity to live electrical circuits or equipment for the purpose of saving life or averting disaster.

British Standard 697 includes recommendations on the maintenance, inspection, re-testing and use of rubber gloves for electrical purposes, and the type normally carried by fire brigades are those which, although they should be tested up to 15,000 volts, should not be used where the voltage is greater than 3,300. The gloves are generally stowed, liberally treated with French chalk, in waterproof metal containers.

Rubber gloves carried on appliances should be examined at the times stipulated in accordance with the *Fire Service Drill Book*.

Rubber mats and special rubber boots are also carried by some fire brigades, usually on emergency tenders, for use in conjunction with rubber gloves, to give an additional measure of protection against injury by electric shock.

*In Chapter 3 of Part 6B of the Manual it emphasises the risks involved by personnel (even when wearing rubber gloves) in coming into contact with live electrical circuits or equipment— especially when water or dampness is present.*

## 21 Asbestos equipment

The use of asbestos as an aid to fire fighting is largely confined to asbestos blankets, which are used for smothering purposes, and to protective clothing, which is used for the protection of the wearer.

### a. Asbestos blankets

Asbestos blankets, in sizes from about 900 to 1800 mm square, are fairly common. They are packed commercially in various types of quick-release containers, which are intended to be fixed in strategic positions in industrial and other establishments, where they can be used to smother small fires. If available quickly enough, they may be used effectively for smothering a person's clothing which has become ignited. Although carried on some fire appliances (usually emergency tenders) asbestos blankets are not very widely used by fire brigades.

### b. Protective clothing

Asbestos protective clothing is not often used by local authority fire brigades (although it is carried on some emergency tenders), but it is frequently to be found as part of the normal equipment of airfield crash tenders. Here its primary function is to facilitate the speedy rescue of persons trapped in crashed aircraft which have caught fire (see the *Manual, Part 6B: Chapter 4, 'Fires in crashed aircraft).*

Various types of asbestos and other protective clothing are produced; some take the form of an *all-in-one* suit, whilst others consist of a helmet, coat and trousers as separate items. Asbestos protective clothing is extremely hot and fatiguing to wear, and the duration for which it can be worn in operational conditions is very limited. Moreover, there is a risk of scalding to the wearer from the production of steam when protective clothing is wetted. It is emphasised in the chapter of the *Manual* dealing with fires in crashed aircraft, that local authority firemen should not wear protective clothing in operational conditions unless they have previously had adequate training and practice in its use and limitations.

Asbestos gauntlets, and also in some cases, face-shields, are carried on some fire appliances to provide protection to hands and face in special circumstances. Special fabrics treated with aluminium have also been produced to reflect heat. Garments made from these fabrics provide protection against intense radiant heat for short periods so long as the outside surface is not tarnished, but there is no application for this type of clothing in the field of general fire fighting.

## 22 Protective clothing for use with breathing apparatus

Protective clothing and masks are used by fire brigades as protection against gases which are skin irritants (e.g. ammonia), and this equipment is described in the *Manual*.

## 23 Medical first-aid equipment

### a. Medical first-aid boxes

All firemen are trained in first-aid treatment of the injured, and a medical first-aid box is normally to be found on every fire brigade vehicle as well as on every fire station. The contents of these first-aid boxes may vary in detail in different fire brigades, but in general they all contain sufficient bandages, slings, sterilised dressings and other items to enable firemen to render first-aid treatment whenever the need arises.

### b. Emergency medical boxes

Many fire brigades hold what are generally referred to as emergency medical boxes. These boxes are comprehensively equipped in collaboration with local medical or hospital authorities and contain, in addition to fairly large supplies of bandages and sterilised dressings, a specially selected supply of drugs and sterilised medical and surgical implements and equipment.

Emergency medical boxes are locked and sealed and held, usually on fire stations, in readiness for use by or upon the direction of a registered medical practitioner at incidents where casualties are involved and where *on-the-spot* medical and/or surgical treatment is an essential and urgent requirement. Adequate safeguards must be taken to ensure that any drugs, the use and storage of which are subject to the provisions of the Dangerous Drugs Act, which are carried in emergency medical boxes are in safe custody and that proper records are kept every time a box is unsealed and any of the contents used. After use, emergency medical boxes must be relocked and sealed until the contents can be checked, replenished and when necessary re-sterilised.

# Chapter 16
# Lamps and lighting sets

A very wide variety of lamps and lighting sets is used by fire brigades and vary from paraffin oil hurricane lamps and battery-operated electric hand lamps of conventional pattern on the one hand to flame-proof safety lamps and mobile and portable floodlighting on the other.

Many of the lamps used are of conventional proprietary makes, and although some of them are illustrated here as typical examples, it cannot be said that any particular type of lamp or lighting set is common to all fire brigades in this country. The choice of lamps and lighting sets is a matter usually determined by local requirements and preference.

## 1 Hand lamps

### a. Electric hand lamps

Various patterns of conventional battery-operated hand lamp are used by fire brigades and usually form part of each fireman's personal equipment, as well as being carried on fire appliances. Most of these lamps have suitable fittings to enable them to be clipped on to a belt or tunic and depend upon dry batteries. General purpose hand lamps are not normally gas-proof and should not be used in conditions where flammable gases and vapours are likely to be present.

### b. Portable electric box lamps

A portable box lamp of one kind or another is usually to be found on every fire appliance for use in conditions where sustained illumination is required and where a hand lamp is inadequate, e.g. for illuminating rooms, stairways and corridors in buildings where normal lighting is not available. A box lamp can be stood on the floor or any convenient ledge and provide illumination of the area in which work has to be done.

The older type of box lamp, illustrated in Fig. 16.1(1), relies on a 6-volt accumulator which must be serviced and periodically recharged. A more modern type (Fig. 16.1(2)) has a 6-volt non-spillable battery, but also incorporates a 2 amp trickle charging unit with a charging indicator light.

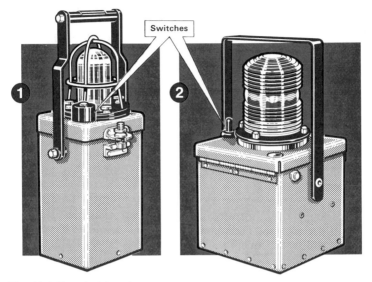

Fig. 16.1 Electrical box lamps.

## c. Safety lamps

These lamps, which are frequently referred to as *B. A. lamps*, are used in conjunction with breathing apparatus in circumstances

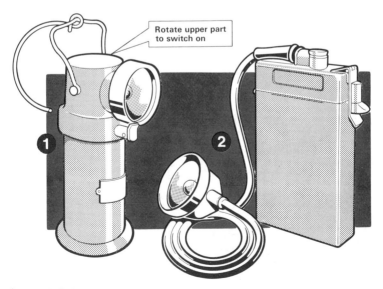

Fig. 16.2 Safety lamps.

where there is danger of the presence of flammable gases or vapours.

Whilst there is no standard safety lamp in use throughout the fire service, a requirement specification issued by the Central Fire Brigades Advisory Council (Specification JCDD/21) gives guidance on safety lamp requirements and recommends that lamps used in the presence of flammable gases or vapours should be intrinsically safe and of a type approved by HM Chief Inspector of Factories for use in the following gases: petroleum, acetone, 'town gas' and coke oven gas. It further states that it is desirable for such lamps to be safe for use also in hydrogen, blue water gas, pentane, hexane, heptane, carbon monoxide, benzene and cyclohexane.

Various types of proprietary safety lamp are used by different brigades and those illustrated in Fig. 16.2 are examples of safety lamps in current use. The one in Fig. 16.2(1) is of the hand lamp pattern, whilst the one in Fig. 16.2(2) has a separate battery container connected by a flexible cable to the lamp unit. The battery container clips on to the fireman's belt whilst the lamp unit is designed for wearing either on the helmet, belt or tunic, thus leaving both hands free. Both types illustrated have rechargeable batteries.

### d. Hurricane lamps

Conventional general purpose hurricane lamps, such as the type illustrated in Fig. 16.3, are commonly used by fire brigades, and although different makes vary slightly in detail, the basic design is much the same and consists of a simple wick-holder fitted into

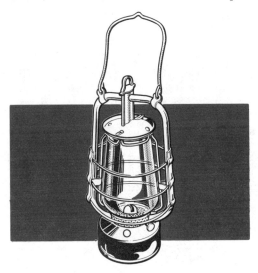

Fig. 16.3 Hurricane lamp.

a paraffin oil container of about 0·56 litres capacity. A glass funnel, surmounted by a ventilated lid and protected by the metal framework of the lamp, provides a partially sealed compartment in which the light will continue to burn even in the highest wind. The only maintenance necessary is to keep the lamp clean, the wick trimmed and the container filled with paraffin.

### e. Testing of hand lamps

Dry battery type electric hand lamps should be checked and tested in accordance with the *Fire Service Drill Book*. Accumulator type hand or box lamps (including breathing apparatus lamps) should also be checked and tested in accordance with the *Fire Service Drill Book*.

## 2 Searchlights and floodlights

Searchlights and floodlights of various kinds are used by fire brigades to provide sustained illumination at the scenes of fires and other incidents. Searchlights are designed to throw a concentrated beam of light which is used for such purposes as illuminating a specific part of an incident (e.g. a rescue from a window high above ground level or where work is confined to a relatively small area). Floodlights are designed to give illumination over a wide area, and are used in circumstances where the whole of a working area requires illuminating (e.g. the whole face of a building or the scene of an accident). The types used can be either electric or pressurised gas or vapour lamp.

### a. Electric searchlights and floodlights

Most fire appliances carry a swivel-mounted searchlight which operates from the vehicle battery and is attached to a reel of flexible cable so that it can be removed from the appliance when necessary and temporarily placed elsewhere. Larger types of electric searchlight and floodlight are usually carried on emergency tenders (Plate 15) where a suitable power supply is available in the form of a built-in or portable generator as well as fixed and/ or portable reels of cable to enable the lamps to be strategically sited at incidents.

### b. Liquefied petroleum gas floodlights

Portable floodlights designed to operate from a cylinder of LPG gas (propane/butane) are used by many fire brigades. One example of this type of lamp is illustrated in Fig. 16.4 and Plate 16 and consists of a strong weatherproof casing which houses a 325 mm reflector and a burner fitted with an incandescent gas mantle. The lamp is connected by a flexible tubing to a reducing valve, and this in turn is connected to a cylinder containing either propane or butane or one of the proprietary mixtures of these gases.

Operation of a main valve on the cylinder feeds gas through the reducing valve to the burner at a working pressure of about 1 bar and the average fuel consumption is approximately 78 litres of gas per hour.

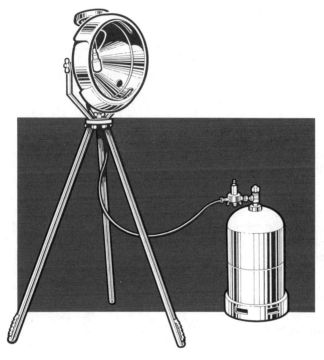

Fig. 16.4 Liquefied petroleum gas (propane/butane) floodlight.

## c. Vaporised paraffin floodlights

Portable vaporised paraffin floodlights have been in common use by fire brigades in this country for many years, and some are still in use today. An example of this type of portable stormproof floodlight consists of a 356 mm in a strong steel casing mounted on a 3·5 litres paraffin oil container. The container is fitted with an oil level indicator and a small force pump similar to those used in 'primus' type stoves and blowlamps.

The lamp is operated by working the pump until sufficient pressure is raised in the container to cause the paraffin oil to flow through a vaporiser to a burner fitted with an incandescent gas mantle. A manually-operated pressure release valve is provided for use when extinguishing the light.

# Structure and publishing history of the
## *Manual of Firemanship*

The *Manual of Firemanship* was first published in a series of nine 'Parts' (1—5, 6a, 6b, 6c and 7) between 1943 and 1962.

In July 1974, it was decided that these nine Parts should be gradually replaced by 18 'Books' and a revised format for the *Manual* was drawn up. The new Books were to up-date the information given and arrange the subjects covered in more compact and coherent groups, each group occupying one of the new Books. The following pages show the original plan, *as amended to date*. Book 5 is the eleventh of these Books to be published.

Since 1974 there have been many developments in Fire Brigade practice and equipment and in the problems which firemen may have to face. To remain an authoritative and up-to-date survey of the science of firefighting the *Manual* must take these developments into account. Not all the necessary changes can be accommodated within the format announced in 1974. The reader should therefore be aware that the structure of unpublished Books of the Manual, as set out on the following pages is subject to change. Such changes will be publicised as far in advance as possible.

The next Book planned for publication is Book 4: 'Incidents involving aircraft, shipping and trains'. This should appear in the form described.

# Manual of Firemanship

**Book 1 Elements of combustion and extinction**
**(published in 1974)**

| Part | *Formerly* | |
|------|------|------|
| | *Part* | *Chapter* |
| 1 Physics of combustion | *1* | *1* |
| 2 Chemistry of combustion | *1* | *1* |
| 3 Methods of extinguishing fire | *1 and* | *2* |
| | *6a* | *32(111)* |

**Book 2 Fire Brigade equipment (published in**
**1974)**

| Part | *Formerly* | |
|------|------|------|
| | *Part* | *Chapter* |
| 1 Hose | *1* | *4* |
| 2 Hose fittings | *1* | *5* |
| 3 Ropes and lines, knots, slings, etc. | *1 and* | *7* |
| | *6a* | *39* |
| 4 Small gear | *1* | *13* |

**Book 3 Fire extinguishing equipment (published**
**in 1976)**

| Part | *Formerly* | |
|------|------|------|
| | *Part* | *Chapter* |
| 1 Hand and stirrup pumps | *1* | *8* |
| 2 Portable chemical extinguishers | *1* | *9* |
| 3 Foam and foam making equipment | *1* | *10* |

**Book 4 Incidents involving aircraft shipping**
**and trains (not yet published)**

| Part | *Information available in* | | |
|------|------|------|------|
| | *Part* | *Chapter* | *Last edition* |
| 1 Incidents involving aircraft | *6b* | *4* | *1973* |
| 2 Incidents involving shipping | *7* | *1—3* | *1972* |
| 3 Incidents involving trains | *6b* | *3* | *1973* |

**Book 5 Ladders and appliances (published in**
**1984)**

| Part | *Formerly* | |
|------|------|------|
| | *Part* | *Chapter* |
| 1 Extension ladders, hook ladders and roof ladders | *1* | *6* |
| 2 Escapes | *2* | *3* |
| 3 Turntable ladders | *2* | *4* |
| 4 Hydraulic platforms | *2* | *5* |
| 5 Special appliances | *2* | *6* |
| 6 Pumping appliances | *2* | *1* |

**Book 6 Breathing apparatus and resuscitation**
   **(published in 1974)**

| Part | *Formerly* | |
|------|------|------|
| | *Part* | *Chapter* |
| 1 Breathing apparatus | *1* | *11* |
| 2 Operational procedure | *6a* | *32(V)* |
| 3 Resuscitation | *1* | *12* |

**Book 7 (first edition) Hydraulics and water**
   **supplies (published in 1975)**

| Part | *Formerly* | |
|------|------|------|
| | *Part* | *Chapter* |
| 1 Hydraulics | *3* | *19* |
| 2 Hydraulics and water supplies | *3* | *20* |
| 3 Water relaying | *3* | *21* |
| Appendices | | |

**Book 7 (second edition)(not yet published)**

As above, plus

| | *Information available in* | |
|------|------|------|
| 4 Pumps, primers and pump operation | *2* | *1—2* |

**Book 8 Building construction and structural ifre**
   **protection (published in 1975)**

| Part | *Formerly* | |
|------|------|------|
| | *Part* | *Chapter* |
| 1 Materials | *4* | *23* |
| 2 Elements of structure | *4* | *23* |
| 3 Building design | *4* | *23* |

**Book 9 Fire protection of buildings (published**
   **in 1977)**

| Part | *Formerly* | |
|------|------|------|
| | *Part* | *Chapter* |
| 1 Fire extinguishing systems | *4* | *24/26* |
| 2 Fire alarm systems | *5* | *28* |
| 3 Fire venting systems | *4* | *23* |

**Book 10 Fire Brigade communications**
   **(published in 1978)**

| Part | *Formerly* | |
|------|------|------|
| | *Part* | *Chapter* |
| 1 The public telephone system and its relationship to the Fire Service | *5* | *27* |
| 2 Mobilising arrangements | *5* | *29* |
| 3 Call-out and remote control systems | *5* | *30* |
| 4 Radio | *5* | *31* |
| 5 Automatic fire alarm signalling systems | *5* | *28* |

**Book 11 Practical firemanship I (published in**
   **1981)**

| Part | *Formerly* | |
|------|------|------|
| | *Part* | *Chapter* |
| 1 Practical firefighting | *6a* | *32* |
| 2 Methods of entry into buildings | *6a* | *35* |
| 3 Control at a fire | *6a* | *33* |

### Book 12 Practical firemanship II (published in 1983)

| Part | Formerly Part | Chapter |
|---|---|---|
| 1 Fire Service rescues | 6a | 36 |
| 2 Decontamination | — | — |
| 3 Ventilation at fires | 6a | 37 |
| 4 Salvage | 6a | 38 |
| 5 After the incident | 6a | 34 |

### Book 13 Contents not yet decided

### Book 14 Special fires I (not yet published)

| Part | Information available in Part | Chapter | Last edition |
|---|---|---|---|
| 1 Fires in animal and vegetable oils | 6c | 45(8) | 1970 |
| 2 Fires in fats and waxes | 6c | 45(3) | 1970 |
| 3 Fires in resins and gums | 6c | 45(13) | 1970 |
| 4 Fires in grain, hops, etc. | 6c | 45(6) | 1970 |
| 5 Fires in fibrous materials | 6c | 45(4) | 1970 |
| 6 Fires in sugar | 6c | 45(15) | 1970 |
| 7 Fires in paint and varnishes | 6c | 45(9) | 1970 |

### Book 15 Special fires II (not yet published)

| Part | Information available in Part | Chapter | Last edition |
|---|---|---|---|
| 1 Fires in dusts | 6c | 45(1) | 1970 |
| 2 Fires in explosives | 6c | 45(2) | 1970 |
| 3 Fires in metals | 6c | 45(7) | 1970 |
| 4 Fires in plastics | 6c | 45(10) | 1970 |
| 5 Fires involving radioactive materials | 6c and 6a | 45(11) 33(VI) | 1970 1971 |
| 6 Fires in refrigeration plant | 6c | 45(12) | 1970 |
| 7 Fires in rubber | 6c | 45(14) | 1970 |

### Book 16 Special fires III (not yet published)

| Part | Information available in Part | Chapter | Last edition |
|---|---|---|---|
| 1 Fires in rural areas | 6b | 1 | 1973 |
| 2 Fires in electricity undertakings | 6b | 3 | 1973 |

### Book 17 Special fires V (not yet published)

| Part | Information available in Part | Chapter | Last edition |
|---|---|---|---|
| 1 Fires in fuels | 6c | 45(5) | 1970 |
| 2 Fires in oil refineries | 6b | 5 | 1973 |
| 3 Fires in gas works | 6b | 2 | 1973 |

### Book 18 Dangerous substances (not yet published)

| | Information available in Part | Chapter | Last edition |
|---|---|---|---|
| Alphabetical list of dangerous substances | 6c | 45(16) | 1970 |

Printed in the UK for HMSO Dd737744 C40 8/84 10170 (1470)